The Circus

by Juanita Casey

Horse by the River, *poems*
The Horse of Selene, *a novel*

JUANITA CASEY

THE CIRCUS

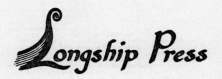

*Set in Pilgrim type and printed
in the Republic of Ireland at
The Dolmen Press Dublin for*

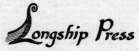

*Crooked Lane, Nantucket,
Massachusetts 02554, U.S.A.*

First United States Edition 1978

ISBN 0 917712 04 8

L.C. 78-55227

FOREWORD

I first became aware of Juanita Casey's writing last year in Ireland while working on a book of contemporary short stories by modern Irish authors (called Paddy No More). *At once, I was taken with the brilliance—I am using the word in the pictorial sense — of her descriptive powers and with her unusual prose style, which led me to include two of her short pieces (*Hemisphere *and* The Well) *in the Longship Press collection.*

Later, Liam Miller, the director of Dolmen Press in Dublin, offered me The Circus *for United States publication. After reading this extraordinary book I felt that Longship Press should make it available to American readers.*

The Circus *deals with the world seen through a child's eyes; a wondrous, sympathetic world of animals and earth, and a jarring, alien world of grown-ups — snippets of inane adult conversation filtering through closed doors. The book culminates in what happens when a young girl finally gets to the circus.*

Juanita Casey is a poet and artist (she drew the circus horse on the jacket) as well as a novelist, and these qualities shine through every page of the book. The Circus *has been called a prose poem rather than a novel, but that is a quibble defining form, not quality. I prefer what an American reviewer wrote a few years ago about her first novel :
'. . . remarkable . . . by a remarkable woman.'*

THE PUBLISHER

Nantucket, Massachusetts
July, 1978

human affairs are dreams. . . .

When I awake the me slides back. Sometimes I jump back into the me, and sometimes I swim, with my head in the me safely, but my tail still stroking sleep at the bottom of the world.

If you look at the pillow with insect eyes, the seam has little gaps in its teeth, and the blanket has a red, Greek fence under my nose. The quilt fields and hills all my bed's country, and everything waits to put on *me*. The day waits to wriggle me into its yellow shoe.

Let me be a bird one day, to wake into the sky's face and fall out of the morning, or a rabbit tickling the air on the dew's carpet. I must begin to *think* all my days now, instead of letting the sun put my coat on, and his hat of daisies. O dear, I say, thinking *me*. And all my years prowling. Why am I? I have a rainbow on my eyelashes, and the sun pulls my warm strings out, like cats lying on steps.

And here I am in a green jersey, thinking *me*, and the sun is bending to look at the tomatoes arriving at red.

Father gives out no strings. Some people wind you in like a warm scarf, but Father shaves and walks about in a vest, with his feet like camels, and reads the paper, and kisses very quick goodnights like wiping egg off. And Mother collapses in leaning, green tents of love, like burying flies in the sugar-bowl. Let one foot come out and half a wing, he struggles and humps like a mole in a sugar field.

You cannot love Mother, ready to sit on you with a spreading octopus, like watching them cut out a cow's stomach all over you.

I will sit on the black hair that used to cover

7

up a bear, and look at Father and Mother. They have eyes and hair and two faces, and smell of eau de cologne and powder and tobacco and armpits and breath and washed hair and clothes, and their teeth in pink glasses. And they read. But they aren't *me*. I was never their very own, full out of love. Somewhere I was born. Somewhere I was given away like kippers. We love you, and they christened me with fine white sugar.

But I must stand back and look at love coming. Like a white bear shaking his head, and his claws tinkling on the gravel, and his black eyes tying me up with a hard string of black watching.

I suppose they put my pram inside the gate, saying Madam like greengrocers with brown paper. I want to *truly* love, galloping, but it only foxes among my trees, and my yellow eyes see it like a run-over frog and don't touch. They are important and want me to love them like Jesus so loved the world. But I cannot. I try in heart's grunts, but except for Thank You for my Birthday, I am grey with salt all round me like an old post in the sea.

I love little crabs and all the easy animals except square-cut dogs, and I think I could love a dinosaur with a great deal of very early love, when only God loved anything, and we hadn't paid him back yet.

Thank you, thank you, to Mother and Father.

But my love yawns with a blue-eyed cat, and velvets into flowers, and if I cup a horse's eye it is lit with no wind blowing my heart out.

We love you. Thank us for finding you. And giving you your bed and your woolly scarf and

8

gloves, and All things Bright and Beautiful done in blue, and my pink soap and nighties, and roast potatoes and a good School, and no dog now but one day. And cupboards and walking sticks and clocks, and books in black and gold specials like God's list.

And I walk on the pavement under strict leaves, filled with loving the grass and the toads and the birds' world. And my secrets left under stones.

And when I go to bed, climbing out of the me to sit amongst the pink flowers beside sleep's blue road, I look under all the secrets, lifting them up like beautiful, transparent stones in green and pink and mauve, and finding where I was born, like the frog in the spring under the old lid.

The child opened and shut the door, swinging. Open and shut. She watched her hand, a spanner of tendons, on the handle, then curling it round the knob like the ball and claw leg of the studded, squashed leather chairs.

I was only saying
   oh the gloxinias are over
       look
You were going to say
      where is?
Chinese or Japanese is it that book on her fifth
        birthday !

 and she
   can't read a word
    Really !

9

> *Ormonde !*
do you know she
> *looks* awfully *like him sometimes I*
>> *wonder*
yes?
> *I stressed and stressed   sssssssst   we* loved *her*
>>>> *her*
> The child hung from the arm, sideways. A spider
was curled in the corner of one panel in the door.
The child saw it was dead, curled into a dry papery
fist of legs, apart. Apart from the hush marks of
the white paint, apart from herself. Apart, apart.
From the draught under the changing door line,
from the discreet, cold hinges. Paint and the small
wind, hinges and open and closing words, and the
spider. All sad. All apart.
> *Noticed yesterday*
>> *flies*
everywhere   we must do
>> *something* (apart, apart)
>> *the*
about
>>>> *flies*

Do not kill the fly :
See how it wrings its hands, its feet.

Mountain is very big for a rocking horse. He canters
on **dancing-class** black hooves, wherever you tell

him, beautifully white, with black spots that romp
all over him, watering at the edges like old men's
eyes in a wind. When you sit on him, your mind
is full up with Mountain, angering at the wallpaper
with his open mouth, and you can get your finger
stuck in his teeth if you try to get his real bit out.
You can plug his tail in through the red crupper.
With him you can go into the pictures, through
the stones and arches by the brown lake, and away
into the lost country no one has ever seen, where
pale hounds statue after a spread stag into a
stiff forest, and someone is riding on a fat little
white horse with snipped ears and poached eyes.
He looks as though he is calling something wide
back to his rider, who has long cockerel sleeves,
stiff feet, and his hat done up on one side like a
fantail pigeon. Some else is running lightly into the
forest with a spear.

Or you can go very light and jingling into a pale,
bright land as delicate as it would be when God
first made it, until we came to it and said, Look,
and the colours hardened and the land known. The
fans of grass are put in just as God would have
said, I think I will have some *here*, and some *there*,
but not there as it won't look right. With rocks;
some with pink flowers on them and a rabbit behind
them. You can see the rabbit, and a doe and her
fawn behind them in the way you know they're
there, but when you say so They say nonsense in
the way grown-ups don't see.

The hawks wear hoods with tufts of bright red
feathers and a bell, and the horses have turquoise
bridles and a long plume under their chins. Some

are like Mountain, and some are blue, dappled with thoughts, some are yellow, some black with long white legs like birch trees. Their tails are like rooks' wings going over. And one is white, with red round him like the bathroom border, and the Shah is riding him. They are all so bright and pale, before the iron of us came. A grey and a black and a white hound point in front of them, tucked for running, and a buck runs between two flower-candle trees. The hounds are not interested in the rabbit. The Shah's trousers are wound up like his best table-cloth, and his jacket is tight with pearls. He points at the buck with a hand full of rings, although everyone is looking except for the last pair near the rock who are talking to each other, being men and women. In the next picture they will bring up the leopards, each one sitting in its cage like a dangerous canary.

The sky is blue, you can't think back any further than the blue, so blue how God must have sighed when he got it right. O Good. Got it at the first go, no messing or changing or turning or mixing, just thinking Light and concentrating Blue, and the sky spreading in one wash of Perfection on his wet page.

On the landing, on a shining white ledge, Father's Colleone and Marcus Aurelius stride towards each other, Colleone trying to see over the bannisters like someone looking over a hedge, Marcus Aurelius Come Forthing like the vicar. He dangles, and has a much nicer face than Colleone's, but he has no reins. If they met, Marcus Aurelius would have to give way to Colleone, with his masterful hand on his reins, sea-urchin spurs, and a proper saddle with stirrups. Both horses are knotted with throaty wrinkles, and both have Behold eyes.

On one side of the stairs, in a picture, a countrywoman sits on a black cow, and drives others in front of her over a bridge. It is all very clear, and one white cow is drinking, and even the gnats over her head are dotted in. You can hear the water trickling down from her chin, it is so clear, and the thuck and rasp of her tongue as she licks it up one nostril and then the other. Perhaps later she gave one of those queer grinding half yawns cows do. A man with his sleeves rolled up sits on the bridge and raises a finger at the countrywoman in her long skirt. She sits sideways, in the dipped middle of the black cow, and doesn't look as though she's seen him. You wonder if he had that sore feeling inside when this happens, and then you don't like to wave again when they do look. And when they've looked away, you misfire your wave again and they're still stone. You're a fool now, and either you look hard past them so that if they look at you again they don't know you've been waving, or you wave at a tree, or a rock and cut them out, however hard they look, and even if they now wave to you.

On the other side, before you say Goodnight and get to the pink wallpaper, there is a difficult, dark painting, as it has gone back nearly to the days when it was painted. There is a big lake, and ruins, and very still trees beside them. Very old trees, and some women are washing clothes in the lake with their vests falling down. They have roped Greek hair and tidied faces, which you wouldn't have

13

really for washing, and one is twisting her ankle pointing. Far away, in a strange country of little trees and rivers and winding roads, all still under the coming thunder, a cheerful centaur is bounding towards them, up and down like a steam-engine. He is very brown, and the horse part of him is a chestnut. The pointing woman looks horrified, but I wouldn't be. It would be nice to have a visiting centaur for company, especially washing clothes. You can think of him on the wet edges of the lake, waving as he canters along, Tittersplat Tittersplat, and whisking at Greek flies.

You wonder what beside the lake is like, sandy like toeing sugar, or sharp like bathsalts, or in slippery bumps like standing on Japanese stone frogs.

There are lions in embroidered silk in the bed-room, and they are the last thing you look at quickly before the light is out. One lioness is already asleep, but the big lion is always Awake and Looking, with one paw turned over, showing its cushions. The gasfire pomps and loses its red toad skin, and it is very important to say three times Goodnight Goodnight Goodnight to the Lion, so that he will never fall asleep and lose you. Because when you're asleep you never know if you're going to fall out of the dream making you You, and get dreamed into another you, far off with thinking, and not yet *you*.

Father and Mother are placed knife and fork together asleep, and somewhere my real father holds a beautiful black dove in his hands, looking around him at the night, which sits a little way off,

14

like a black fox. He throws the dove up and it
flies towards the moon, away and away with my
father's white face looking up, floating like a flatfish, turning white as it swings away searching for
me in the night, where I am thinking *my father*.

And my mother is asleep with no thinking at all,
in a skirt of green grass, and her hair is bound with
nettles which do not hurt her. A stag steps over
her sleep and she doesn't stir, and he flicks his tail
as he grazes. A line of swallows sleep with her, their
pronged feet all down her shoulder and on her cool
arm. And she and they will wake together, with no
thinking at all, preening and stretching.

> *If you walk, just walk.*
> *If you sit, just sit.*
> *But don't wobble, whatever you do.*

Just against your leg Marion
    that's all I ever ask   God am I now
so bloody revolting you can't manage even that
    May   May for God's sake
Oh it isn't that
        Then what the hell is it   oh
I don't know   I   oh I wish you wouldn't smoke so
much   its   its not just me   I know it happens to
honestly   all women
        You're always bloody tired always morning noon
                                    and night

bloody tired　　　　　　　*Oh* please *Gee　no*
　lovely and warm there　oh Gee no
　*The child is sitting up in bed, with the stars
creaking and singing and crackling and wheeling
through the night. And the mind which is all the
night. As though the worlds are a flight of great
phosphorescent whales diving through time.*

　Oh Gee for heaven's sake　all over　*no it isn't
I used paper*

　*Diving through Time.　Whales, whistling and
tuning, and brushing through the stars' crystalline
nets and the moon a-clang with their echoes.*

　NO　*Only joking* Mother　*I tell you what I was
thinking of begonias down the front drive this
year　Mmm　ah well night night*

　Gee I do love you　really I do
　Ah
　　　　I know
　　　　I know
　　　　　　　Night night

There were two worlds. One was of carpets
with thickness, of blue and green and red, and you
could go along with them and the red would turn
into a big curling flower, and the blue would repeat
itself like money in the corners. The green would
nibble around them like a sheep, making paths
that led into the blue money mazes, and then went
on to join the red, and be leaves and stems for its
stiff flowers. There were lion-yellows in the carpets
too, not like sunlight on grass through beechleaves,

but fenced in black to go with the money and the flowers, and forced to sit amongst them in a pattern of biscuits. The stairs had the same carpet, and the flowers were choked down with brass rods over their throats, and the money divided and triumphed on one step, and then an escaped biscuit. It was important to try and miss the biscuits and walk firmly on the money, which would have been wonderful for an elephant. He would have fitted his blue feet exactly onto the squashed money, and tumped down the hall, carefully keeping in them all the way, and then down onto the tiles. If he looked out through the blue and red glass at the front door, he could see the garden astonished with blue, or drowned waving under red. He could manage the front door's knob if he was careful, and then he would bend out through it, stepping over the scraper and rattling the letter-box which said Letters in pythons. No one would have seen him, he would have been so quiet on his sofa feet, not touching the letters lying on the mat, squared like a small harsh piece of buffalo. Someone would have said I'm sure that was the front door, and the grandfather clock would say Tin as they went by, which he always did if anyone passed him. No one ever noticed him until he got ready for Time inside him, and then he would struggle for the golden space between two black ticks, and stifle what he wanted to say so that all he said was one Er Spung. He looked different at his hours. At twelve o'clock he looked up both together at his wooden crown and spunged past counting, and sighed afterwards as though the last one had been hard. At one o'clock

17

and ten he looked uneasy, and at quarter to nine and three as though he was going out somewhere; he looked excited. At seven and four he came back thinking It's getting on, but six he loved. He was happy at six, as though the world was coming right, and he could stretch his black spears right through the poached egg they went around, with the hole in the middle to wind him up with St. Peter's lost key. At six he said Babylon clearly and not Spung, which is a lovely golden word, shot with red. At times, when he was corrected, which he hated, he buzzed like a fly in a stable web before his tick could run back like a flea off the end of the key, and if he was made to spung before he wanted Time to come, he said Haddock very rudely. It was surprising they didn't say How dare you say that, it's a forbidden word. But as he went to bed inside, as well as living in his wood, they couldn't very well. Forbidden was a pink city word, with sharp turrets and no one living in it. You tried to catch him asleep. If you opened the door quickly and pretended to shut it, but didn't, you might unhinge the ticks, but he never fell for it. He was not allowed to spung at night because sleep and spunging growled at each other on the landing, but you could tell if you were awake when the big hour came, because he gasped and buzzed and then clicked. You felt that he was comforted when a tick came at once to say It's alright. The click was blind. It felt its way out of his face like a beetle on fishook legs, tapping on the spongy, sagging darkness.

Is not this Reality?
It is, but it's a pity to say so.

The other world of the servants' hall was down three brown lino stairs through a door which swung breathing out, white on our side like the rest of the wood, and green baize like silver-polishing aprons on their side.

There was coal smelling of cats and iron down the passage opposite the kitchen, and a pantry full of fishknives, and loud cupboards which smelt of soap and wet dogs and ammonia. The kitchen was full of faces saying go away and o no let her in, and a scuffle in the sitting-room as Mr. Dodds the chauffeur came out and aprons going on. Of soup and onions and wooden spoons, making tea, and a ginger cat ribbed like the tide out.

The scullery had an untidy girl all to itself, full of red soap and smelling of sick. There was always talk of mice, and although you never saw one you could smell them sometimes, like hot sawdust.

The sitting-room was warm, with fat chairs and cushions smelling of Cook, who smelt more of humans than anyone else, and built-up cookings like bricks, and loose cabbage hair. She had true knives, intense and thinly aware of the sweet wood of the kitchen table. The wood had long silvery seams like celery, and smooth knuckled knots in pauses.

You could listen under the windows, inside the laurels which grieved when it drizzled, with yellow spots. They held each other sadly and tapped when they were ill. You heard talk not a part of the thick carpets, more interesting and going up your backbone. Separate like smoking and the pink city.

The back stairs had scrubbings and hollow box noises, and horse chestnut bannisters in streaks like clumsy paint brushes.

Ours were white, without dust, and with diamonds and rounds to alter your eyes to look through, and they elbowed the stairs away like well bred people in a crowd, not rudely but leaning them round into a corner where all the reds and the blue money and the biscuits were able to spread out again. The bay bannister was horse colour, shining fast down into a rushing chow's tail, a curling Amen which was completely final.

There was an unhappy, brown fringed bit where the hall carpet and the stairs met, no reds or blues but brown felt there, like mummies. It was nice to pretend to lose sixpence there and warm finding it, knowing it wasn't really lost to the grey scurry of true loss. Other people walked over it and you could smile, like God watching the sparrow fall and no one else knowing.

The backdoor had a stone passage to it, where puddles would be if it rained. There were boots and dogs' leads and string and cows' halters and raincoats smelling of old sheep. Sometimes a coat or a scarf which you mustn't touch, which made you feel like stealing dogs, made you not look in case you knew absolutely into touching. The backdoor was unloved, with a high glass window above it that had looked out on something dreadful, even though it was so high and shaped for not looking. The backdoor key was heavy and black, not like St. Peter's key, but desolate and old. It could lock the doors behind which they killed dark red bulls, or hung up Bluebeard's wife with white tiles all round, and a grating in the stone floor and red and blue glass in the window so that you wouldn't see at first.

One of the rows of bells hanging like pears would jerk like someone pulling a tired horse's mouth to trot, and they would run, Who is it. Number 3. Theres' no Number 3 now. There's no one there. There's no number 3 now, and they try the door just in case. Don't go in, don't look. And Murder which is blue and red in gulps.

It was really an old larder with a rusted butter churn and a pram, and a smell of pine-tree roots in mould, and green coming in through the little wire holes, nearly all holes in the wire over the windows. A blackbird had flown against it once. O go and kill it. O Mr. Dodds, the poor thing. He had held it up, and it had bled in sprays over the laurels. The leaves rusted with the drops, and always had dark spots on stiff-winged leaves afterwards. You hadn't noticed before that they were different to the yellow spots of the other side, where the sun came to tea with Mr. Dodds and the talk. A mouse died there too. You nearly walked on him, and he was flat with old death and rusty, and he looked angry as though he'd walked on himself and said Ugh. You're always in the shrubberies. Why don't you play on the lawn. I don't know. Funny child. No one laughs with funny.

I wonder if the elephant broke that branch off as he went out; he must have stuffed in the acorns as well. Pigs died of too many acorns. But they couldn't hurt an elephant. How could you get him out, you hadn't thought. He couldn't push down the iron railings onto the main road. You stood together in the big shrubbery, under the royal cloak of the red rhododendron which was big enough to hide him. He ate a whole hand of crimson as you thought together. A caterpillar fell on you, like a soft green L. Then it twisted into a C and fell off into the mould. The elephant flapped one ear, and rattled the shiny leaves. His toenails shone in the earth like pale toadstools. As he was clever he could undo the front gate if I hold up the long pin that keeps it shut in its hole.

He comes after me. We go right through the shrubbery, and he takes another head from the white rhododendron with the bumblebee centres. I hope he doesn't take a real bee for elephants are known to go mad, and I'll get the blame and he could go and wreck the church.

Breathless, we manage the gate together, and he goes out and waits for the traffic. Then he crosses the road and sways off towards town looking like a statue that hasn't been unveiled. That is very clever of him, as it will put people off. So long as no one pulls his tail, when it will fall off and the whole elephant appear. Goodbye. He can't say it back so he plays all I can remember of the Trumpet Voluntary until he gets down to the War Memorial, where we have arranged together that he disappears.

A barrier is a brick with which to knock at
a door.
When the door opened the brick may be
thrown away.

The larder also looked out over more laurels,
fly-blown with talk that came out through the
window of the servant's hall; different smaller
spots, like the full-stops they left on the glass, the
talk falling on them in dots. The larder was very
cold and white, with boathooks from the ceiling.
The same green came in, and meat and ham sat
heavily under musical wire covers like combs, and
cucumber slices fainted over each other in vinegar,
like thin waterlillies in a sharp brown pond.

The joints were always on blue dishes with a
faraway world on them that made you curiously
sad. There were cows in water, and cottages like
haystacks, and a flock of birds over the tall elm
trees. A woman fed chickens from her apron, and
it was so quiet in the bright blue country. A heron
was nailed up on the cottage wall. The country was
gone, which made you regret with a sore heart,
not the sadness which comes into your throat as
well, and then tears, but dreadfully sad because it
is impossible and gone, and however much you
look and Try, it will never be again.

Some houses did it, and some trees and parts of
places. With a corner, or the way the sun held
himself in a wood, or a moment in what they called
a view, which was an infinite going on while

standing still. Places by a wall did it, and places with nothing but grass and leaves composed in shadow with a fern, which made you feel dark in church. Not people saying and doing, but the leaves folded in perfection and the grass utterly faithful. The fern was like a prayer, but a complete and right one, immediate and without words, which was in you as you looked, and didn't start Our Father or O God in velvet mustiness and mauve cushions. Mice smelt of church badly. And sometimes it came with the kind of light, making you look up through cherries with your hands in pink and blue, when the cuckoo joins the tree heads together with cuckoo on a long thread like water, and it is still cold and very blue.

Or when the sun is tired with the summer and the lawn smells of grass lines, and the turtle doves reel the heat up and down the ash trees, and pull summer along on little forever wheels. Sometimes they come down on the drive, very soft and humble, but turn into flying fans, ringed and necklaced with black and white tail pearls across the fast air.

Little buggar's at it again Maudie what eavesdropping again that kid'll never make it Mr. Lightfoot mark my words never fit in   Talk about a silk purse outa sow's ear Cah   that Mr. Ormonde women and 'orses. Specially 'orses. gypsy kid indeed must've charmed 'im somehow   picked it up orf of em if you arst me   well I'm not standing for anything   slightest sauce from that and I'm off off   Bloody cheek

24

Ah I dunno Cook   Por little fucker. Allo Little
Fucker   what you doin' there then   Mr. Lightfoot
What's that then d'you know that kid's got lovely
eyes, reely lovely   *What's that then, Deffy a*
Hephalant   A por little mouse   Hey Maudie what
about a great big bull helephant   Oh Tom no   No
Cook make 'im stop it   *Oh Mr.* Lightfoot   *I'll* tell
Oh 'e's a scream   Reely 'e is

Nobody seems to know. Nobody *sees*. Everyone
prays and says We must have no secrets. These are
true secrets, with long monkey arms round you,
because no one else sees them and you don't feel
sore in the heart with wanting Unknown very
deeply, in the way that ferns are, and the far blue
country of the larder plates. The Unknowns are
deeply *me*, utterly stretched secrets into long regrets
of Nevermore, past all the stars to the end of the
world going backwards and forwards.

Have Faith, be faithful. At Christmas, with an
organ, no one sees the fern has faith all the time,
and its shadow in the afternoon. The feeling shades
away like the edges of sheep in winter, which the
mind opens up with show, and the snow cuts out
black secrets like warmth going. And the grass,
which is never ugly, is faithful however rough the
place is, like looking out of a waiting carriage and
only grass on the built bank. That is faith, and faith
lies all along the ground in between the stones, and
still goes on even if your shadow stands on it, or
the fern dies back into brown fur, or the toad
prince isn't at home under the rockery.

Great faith forever and ever Amen, ends in the stars which even God can't touch. O it's cold. Out there, out where even he doesn't want to go, and he leaves them, and gets on with the world. Sometimes they howl, the stars. They are full of black dogs' hearts, and children who have missed heaven And they are icy with feeling too much of secrets, and because they get our Wantings and our greatest feelings of O God, they completely *know*. And the furthest ones are regretful with the longing of our knowing, and the nearest ones return a child sometimes.

The old pond.
A frog jumps in.
Plop !

She doesn't say *anything Gee she just stands there*
No response no warmth *I tell her we* love *her we Really Do Love her and those* a chrysanthemum head snaps *queer green eyes she just* looks *Do you know you know I was thinking Ormonde said* knitting *gypsies never give their children up didn't he say other tribes or families or whatever take them over sometimes she's so* like *Ormonde by some girl I feel she oughtn't to* know *this background adopted yes but not* a gypsy *only hope Ormonde never* the afternoon

proceeds in slow hops and pauses dreary and drug-
ged as a sick rabbit *oh wasn't that   listen Gee
listen the telephone* the green cushion, fat and
braided, sags, is comforted again into its plump
fatuous triangle *oh   how lovely Mrs.* Templeton
oh how   yes
            yes
                    yes
*what   ohyes Doyouknow we were just saying
we'd not seen you or dear Laurence for   what   yes
dear we'd simply love to Sunday at 4 lovely
lovely Bye dear Bye* Bombers again attacked
the coastal ports of *Gee, have you seen my knitting* casualties are reported heavy among fleeing
civilians *under the cushion*
                    ah
The afternoon. The sick rabbit. Are dead.
                            yes

   It was in the bathroom that they said, We love
you just as much, and it makes no difference. It
smelt warm of the white towel off the radiator.
We don't know who they really were they said,
but we love you even better. There were hundreds,
picking in the white knots of the towel, and we
chose *you.* You choose by pressing the pops on the
wallpaper, like seaweed. Not all popped, some
escaped politely like people raising their hats and
I must get on, and some died with your thumbnail,
quietly. The best you chose didn't squirt sea, but
popped and went in, staying, the roundness gone in.

27

It was pleasant like pressing paint skin, giving in like eyes and lurking with pleasure, until the full plurt and windings-up of a round, coloured satisfaction.

You were left at this big house, and the clean sheets' smell. You were like Wee Willie Winkie left running over the town because the star threw him back. He was cold on the doorstep when they found him. Perhaps the star didn't return me, but I was born, feeling like blankets. I sat in the darkness, in warm skins with a wolf coming in. Found, they would have said, finding.

Finding means the sun and dogs' faces at five tea o'clock, and the darkness falls back with the wolf, tipped like pine trees. And I want to go back. Dost thou know who made thee, I a child and thou a lamb. Look what the lambs are doing. Mr. Loving will you cut plenty of mint. Chop it like sparrows' legs and tie it with straw in combed horse waves in the potting shed. Mr. Loving smells of black hair and boxes, his hands toad in the soil and he gives you a peach like women. What do you say. He lost his son when the begonias went to the war, and it was a hot summer back in the cream cakes. Their heads fell off because of the thunder, and they need a lot of water because of their flesh. Mr. Loving do you know I was lost too, but got found again. By a wolf, a mother. He scratches his head with his finger like chimney bricks. You'll get a slap.

Slap !
'There ! Why don't you wipe the dirt off your
own face.'

Words come round like the hours, some treacle
slowly and some overtake and strike. Goodness, is
that the time. Mind now. Out of it. What. Hallo,
sweetie. *Don't* walk on that. Mind they're fresh,
the eggs, and lettuce, and strawberries.

Maggie the housemaid is bathing the terrier in
the sink with redbrick soap and hippo's arms. He
is pressed down with soap and dismay, and spiders
his paws over the china sink's manger edge.

Eggs isn't a nice word, it should be warm and
brown rolling, gently. Egg is a gum word, too short
and thick, and it should belong to nests and the
slow-worm legs of the teacosy hens that have red
and green like church windows deep in their brown
feathers. Except for the finger-wire pen of blacks,
with pink foxglove combs and neatness like small
parlourmaids, and black tails up like knights. They
lay chalk eggs so white it has gone into itself and
can't go any further past white, and some have
chips all over them like picking up little teeth on
roundness. They step brightly and flicker their heads
with the wind in the nettles, and skid along and
jump after flies. The browns are mothers who dust
in the hollows, and stretch like feather hammocks
beside their tar house with asleep lizard's eyes, and
one wing out like a run-over.

The Father is white and necklaced like a Zulu, he

29

warriors and walks with firmness, with his tail in many black C's which leaf and green and blow when he turns. He decides, and is so definite he echoes. When he looks at you, he chisels and smalls the part he looks at, drilling looks with yellow and black dots. Sometimes he yawns and his sword tongue la-las. Some of the crossed hens have Indian brass collars and bronze-fingered feathers like very exact angels and some are mothers in little runs bending to look in the grass, and plump and tock in circles with primrose chicks. They dip and oar round their own feet like boats, all defending mother caves, and one chick stands and hiccups without thinking it is itself. It has lost what it is in the sunlight, and closes its eyes and peeps. And then it will find its running and ticking again, after her. When she sits they part through her curtaining breast feathers, their world of comfort, as we are like eiderdowns on a frosty night. And she dozes in and out in small huffs like a bellows. Her world is them and her coop in the grass, and then there is the orchard and the fence, the gardens and the fields and houses, the town and more country, and then England and the sea. All worlds to everything and us, and then the whole world which we know because it's told us by the people and God. *They* seem to know so much, like sheets laid out to dry over bushes, and some are coloured towels with design minds, but you want to say, when they say It's only a hen and she can't know, that she isn't just alive in her coop *now* in the world, but you are her too, not divided like sums in a black line, but overlapping like roofs and feathers and sunlight and night, in affection and deep knowing.

The orchard has waves of great apple trees which break against the wood and spray back into small, wilder ones that have blown into the hedges. Some have grown tired of holding up so many green years and red apples, and their branches bend elbows in the grass. Sometimes you will find apples wrinkled and gone-down like lost brown balloons, and sometimes when you pick them up you find they are still growing on the bough, and it gives you a shock of unexpected, like finding wild eggs in a nest or seeing a rabbit nearer to you than the pullback of the tree's fingers. The trees with green apples are cold, with white blossom and military shelf cookers. They don't bend or star into pink outbursts like the red apple trees, but stand perfectly. The pink ones sing and clang their apples like bells, when the sun hangs over the mists like a red apple too. With the mists that scarve and wrap summer away from the autumn, the apples drop like a horse's hoof on the grass. And you can hear a rain of one by one apples rolling down through the branches like stairs on sharp fox nights.

Our two lives.
Between them is the life
Of the cherry-flowers.

Sister Anne, sister Anne
she fell into the
                             frying pan
isn't that
            FUNNY?
Never touch *a razor*

The cherry trees are white, some with black and some with red cherries. Their trunks have the mauve bloom of whippets. They don't throw out their blossom like the apples, but receive it like crowns, and are the beautiful rulers of the orchard. The apples may lean on each other, and put sprays of pink feet onto another's white cushion, but cherries cry pink up all around and then stand, like fountains. The long blue ladder will four feet up into them, and Mr. Loving's black cat snakes up it sometimes looking for birds. She hops from step to step, and is horrible like black-gloved fingers over a piano. She lamps in the branches after the little birds, sliding like oil that runs and stops and runs down a road, and sometimes when there is a wind, flying like a piece torn out of a bigger shadow. Mr. Loving's wife is like a bird. She is very small, with rook's eyes and pecks goodmorning seeds with a sharp nose. Loving strokes the cat and tells her good pussy in a voice for wives, but the cat receives it all down her harsh back in twitches. Mrs. Loving sings when he speaks to the cat, doing something very loudly. In their cottage Mrs. Loving preens her hair with her hands like a swan doing his back, and lifts lids. She put on small aprons with frills and heart pockets, and her washing line has lots of different ones, mauve and peach and green and pink, which tickle Mr. Loving's helpless combs and his flayed shirts. His socks hang together right down at the far end of the line like bats, as though Mrs. Loving doesn't like them up among the aprons. Sometimes she has skinned-rabbit pink nighties, and pale blue ones which let the sun in through curtains, and she likes nice as a word, which she says very often like a sugar bowl with pink roses.

Mr. Loving sits by his grate and the cat has the other chair with velvet, the cat pulling over comfort with her paws, and Mr. Loving with his feet in slippers like flat hares. The windows jangle and flamingo with big fuschias, and a plant with spotted purses reigns in the middle of the flowered table cloth, in a dark green china pot with people hunting a stag all round it in the Greek days. It is very definite it's there, and you feel it should be asked before you clear the table. It hears news, and you wonder what happens to all the news when we've finished with it. It weasels along to the socks outside, and to some empty gnashing pegs, and the fence catches the words and straightens them up and down and the weather buzzes on the tar. The path has grass and stones and one dandelion and lies down flat so that no news gets caught on any bumps, and then the white rhododendrons get booms of music down their central ears, and tuck away bits of weather, patting it under their leaves. Pink Pearl is too far, and makes her own weather and flowers, receiving bees and the sun and thinking pink into people who pass. So deeply pink they gasp. Even at night she rings with pink and won't give in, even to the moon. You can sit inside her, and she breathes and presses pink into your nose and eyes, and you hear pink lying like the sea against your ears. She hums pink out into the warmth, and bees hurray around her. The sun stays with her all day, from the morning when she leans out with the dew and fines the day around her like pillows, until she withdraws into a mauve for night, although she still keeps pink with her. It is dry under her when it rains. She is a mother too, like the hens.

Other rhododendrons are different. In the dell they are dark red with black mouths, and their trunks snake and are rusty. Something is buried near them, but you can't tell what it is, only that it is under the leaves and the silence, and is white and chalky and eaten away, and the silence runs in white threads under the roots.

A Chinese tiger looks out from the sword grass with petal whiskers, but he is not hurtful. There is only one place he can see out through the spotted lilies, but if you went after him he would get very large and dark and press back under the rhododendrons to attack. It is best to let him alone by his lilies as he only wants you to see that he is there, with his orange and white lips, and a black scroll on his forehead like a written butterfly, which says he is Chinese.

On very hot days the dell smells of tiger, and he yawns and grins under the leaves with his tail striping in and out of the red and green shadows.

Then you mustn't see him at all, but think of tea
and hum and look only at the path, and try not to
smell back. He gets nervous near thunder, and you
mustn't hurry. But when you walk on the big black
flint at the top of the path you're safe and can
look back, as he can't come out now whatever
happens. Only in thunder, when he runs through
the rain in silver leaps, and bellies from tree to tree
because he is afraid. In winter he turns white, and
goes back to China.

> The butterfly having disappeared,
> My spirit
> Came back to me.

Frank! *not* here.
Come on, come on. Doll, come on
J-just for me, please, *Doll. No one's about*
Come ON
O orlright. Lemme hang up your shirt first — go
on — you randy thing —
ah *Frank*, wait.
If they see us — wait now. Frank
First me suspender
Frank !

T't Look — you dirty devil —

35

They are netting the cherry trees. Father and Mr. Loving hate the blackbirds that get into the net. Loving lets the cat in to chase the birds, and they flutter and hang themselves. Mr. Loving picks them off the net and kills them, and the cat runs with one in her mouth, which cries. They kill the sparrows that get into the raspberries and the currant cages, and you know these are fathers and mothers too. The north sky eggs of the blackbirds they smash from their mossy homes, and there is blood and their string babies all over the path.

God sees the sparrows die, but he never strikes Mr. Loving, and the blackbirds go on singing. They nail up roofed wooden homes for the other birds, and they say isn't it lovely to hear the birds. And Mr. Loving hangs all the birds he catches up on a line like Mrs. Loving, but the line smells of dried death with no crying. It is in the kitchen garden, and there are two stoats that swing like stiff chamois-leather socks, and the wind gets caught on their teeth as it goes into their black dry mouths and through their whistling bodies, and a magpie clattering like old pens, and some rooks that circle and point white compass heads and clenched feet holding onto blindness and holes. A new jay is astonished into death with his loud blue eyes still open, pink and tidy black, and the flashing scream still blue on his wings.

Don't go too near, there's a snake that can still bite. It won't die until the sun goes down. It hangs broken and quite still, and its blood is red and usual. You expect it to have green blood, and be rare. The sun has written on it, with a thick black pen, and you think of its second death in the dark, the first having happened to it now, the second will take the Devil out and it will be quite dead from men. Its eyes are divided like night from day, perhaps that is why it has to die twice for us. Over its head the scales roof it, and they are like spades that have turned over and pressed the snake in, all the way down to its flip.

. . . Hither and thither, reading book after book
And looking for someone who would spare a
*   drop of water*
To keep alive the gudgeon in the carriage rut.

There used to be an angel near the walnut tree, but while the snake is there he won't stay. They always hit the tree whenever they pass it, with a stick, but they don't see the angel who sits by the hedge and reads a lot. He never speaks because he can't, and his wings are made of leaves, not feathers, and he's quite happy to be on earth. He doesn't fly, and doesn't seem to have much to do with God. You hit the tree too, but gently so as not to hurt the angel who can feel it in his wings. It is a pity the snake is there, as although you can go and find other nice places yourself for the angel to sit in, it doesn't work.

He has to *be*. You can't show him, or put him where you want to, or where you think he wants

37

to be, even where he thinks he'd like to be. He has to *be*, nowhere else and without you or he or God thinking it. And the snake may spoil it, and if you *think* him it will spoil it, and with angels it is forever.

The toad prince is really there, and likes the rain. He is not like the angel who depends on the sunlight, for when it rains he can't read and goes into the walnut tree. The toad prince lives under a stone in the Japanese garden. His home is filled with melancholy like a stone urn, hanging mauve flowers divide overhead, and inside there is green moss and his bronze eyes.

When no one is looking, you take one of the thin Japanese saucers out of the moth and velvet cupboard from under its small cup. It is blue, like raining with blue and white flowers, very cold and small and right for the toad prince. It looks very lost by the stone as it hasn't taken its world there with it. The stone and the saucer don't mingle together like the flowers, or a leaf with the stone. They are cold and sad and terribly apart. The toad sometimes comes out and puts his hand on the saucer with the water in it, on a hot day. He doesn't look at it, and his hand slides over the blue and white flowers and the blue lady on the bottom. He tips it up and moves his hindleg on to it. He leaves the saucer with no water in it, and walks through the mauve hanging flowers without dipping his head. He shuts his eyes when he goes under them and spreads the flowers down with reaching hands. He goes slowly and feels stones, closing his eyes when he stops, and tasting himself. Sometimes he isn't under the stone, and must be walking some-where. Through all the grass, pushing himself under the venomous primulas, and the plants with dish leaves. When he is home his eyes shine for a hundred years behind you, and he feels like Buddha. Behind him there is a dark rhododendron with yellow flowers going up like here and there candles, and when you have gone he sits all through the night being himself.

It makes you feel lonely when you think of him in the night with the world growing.

When it rains, the saucer will be full of water in the morning, and it will smell of melancholy going back and to come. It is magic by the stone, before people.

You can't be a toad, even if you try. You can get down to pretend, but thoughts keep you out of toad like high railings. It is you being a toad, and that's no good at all. And he can't be you. All you have is you and he is himself, and your world is together for a little while under the smell of the melancholy and the hundred years. It is almost the same with the angel, except you can't ponder like you can with the toad. With the angel you mustn't look or catch thinking him, because it will harden into nettles, and you mustn't think he is or he isn't. As he just *is*. Thinking traps rabbits, and can never roll in the sun.

The crocuses look well.
M'mm

I suppose they're right about the . . .
         birds? O dear, it's . . .
a blackbird, too many Gerald says but

Cover the mirrors   don't touch knives
it's going to
                    thunder

    'I, E-cho, ask you "What is the Buddha?" '
    Hogen answered 'You are E-cho'.

Sometimes it is a good thing to go and be properly sad, so that you can be happy. Under the farewell pine trees which creak and sigh like boats there is the horse's tomb. It is surrounded by mauve rhododendrons and iron railings, and has a big stone with *Prince* and *Marquis* on it in iron. The grass is thin and soft like a foal's mane, and pine needles fall over the flat stone like a plate of fish bones.

Melancholy has gone past up the path, and only a feeling of long bones is left. They were carriage horses, and lifted their feet high over the gravel, looking blind and shining. They must lie very long in death, with their skulls hearing themselves further and further away, and their hooves making teacups for death.

They took ladies to church, Father says, by the green lawns. They shone and waited near the

40

flowers. Then the cars came and they waited by
the stables, on the gravel, for the vet. Unblinded in
old halters. The ladies thought they were merciful,
as they were old aged. But someone saw. They
kicked and fell down and they cried in agony, for
the vet used acid, and then they shouted Hold them
over the drain. One banged his tail even when he
was dead and the other cried like a real person,
Mr. Loving said, with tears creeping like ants.

Now their death echoes twice in bone circles
and their teeth won't let go of evermore. The
rhododendrons lay down flowers all over them, and
they are mauve together.

You say forgive us our trespasses because evil
can be mauve too, and they must forgive us. If you
say Amen it helps them. They have forgotten, but
if you mean it in the heart's sadness it helps everyone, and the world too. And happiness can come
out of the corners again towards God.

You must say Amen six times and go backwards,
and then they can go to their heaven properly.

This isn't like the toad or the angel, you have
to think all over to keep them up there when you're
gone. They smoke back, seeing mauve, which is
important that you leave them some other flowers
when the rhododendrons have gone, and then they
can go back again. And the stone must never move
like Jesus. They can never hurt again, and they can
take happiness up with them in the sun's dust
coming down through the pines if you say Amen,
and Forever and ever, and they can walk steadily
back past the sun, nodding and swishing their long
tails, the poor old horses and their long ago.

That was old Polly look   white as snow   and that's a landau and there's GrandFather's little black pug look   what marvellous photography then crystal clear

There is a crystal now, Now. It has been for four hundred million years and will be in another four hundred million years. Perfect. Now. Then. When oh when, when . . .

She was over 40 they say. Poor old Polly   snow white Prussic acid   oh how awful   I mean a horse But I believe they still use it on cats, Gee — terribly quick   I believe
                    in the eyes
    Deffy a bun take a bun

A bird grieving in the wind that the Emperor's horses are gone. . . .

One day the toad prince will die too. He might glove on the road from a car, with blood and his yellow stomach, or somewhere even God can't find, looking through the grass for sparrows; and you must die, locked up in white, and different angels telling God you are dust, with Judgement waiting like a black spaniel with sad red eyes. Father and Mother must die, which is why you must behave, but this isn't sad yet, as it goes away under the copper beeches for when you are grown up.

The dogs' graves are near the rows of violets, which Mr. Loving picks like handfuls of mauve donkeys' ears. The dogs have a stone with stone names cut out, and the violets smell of regret and retrievers, and the cherrypie grows on a collie. Wallflowers divide a pug into pansies, and people smile. You make a cross of sticks and wool for the birds, which are sometimes calm little tits in a comfort of blue and yellow death, and sometimes a blackbird with an orange word nearly out, and if you find a sparrow you bury him very carefully and say Amen slowly, as God has counted him. You mustn't take the real flowers, so you pick them daisies for their jamjars, and buttercups for happiness. Once an owl went very tired into death, with a yawn and brooch feet. His face was like a clock with no time, and he was speckled like eggs and jewels, with precious feathers as soft as blowing. He had a red barley-sugar candle, specially for his death.

I think it was the kindest
Ah, yes
Messing all over the place like that. She couldn't have been happy
oh, no, you can't keep a dirty dog on   *You'd better tell Ormonde.*
And keep Deffy away. I couldn't face him. I'll think of something to tell her tonight
Nembutal, Mrs. Harding   oh absolutely painless

Poof Deffy will be sad I'm afraid   she was a real
Peter Pan dog wasn't she. Oh I think you must tell
her and straight away
    But wasn't she your mother-in-law's dog   oh I
see   yes   yes   I see

They covered Patsy up in the potting-shed with
four thick sacks. She came back in the car, and Mr.
Loving helped Mr. Dodds carry her. Patsy was as
big as Cook and was ill for too long. She lay on the
white rug and slept all day, and they said we really
must do something about Patsy because of suffering.
The vet said they must take her back After. Mr.
Loving said why the hell did they want a St.
Bernard, and said six feet at least like a bloody
human. You hope Patsy won't be near hell. Her
black face is all fallen down under the sacks and
her pink begonia eyes that feel worry, and Mr.
Loving is hateful to put Patsy near hell and say
bloody even though she's dead.
    Go away and you shouldn't look. A nose in
everything. Patsy's fat is all cold and sticks. Her
buttons have gone mauve and cold, and so has her
big mouth. Suddenly it is terrible, and tears come
on like large cats, pricking very large and hot. They
put her right away from the violets, but she has
foxgloves which are like her face. Mr. Loving writes
PATSY on a piece of paper with a short square
pencil he uses for labels, and says why do you want
it. She has no stone yet, but she can have her name
put under four stones on the corners to remind God.

She will have to have another piece if it rains forgetting.

Death must be filled with everyone all different, being everyone with their names, and finding birds, and Patsy gone very new. God straightens the people out for heaven, and takes out lambs, and the devil takes all the goats for hell.

The Tramp's boots have nails like horseshoes. He snores like a flat, black pig and smells of wasps in jars. Pink Pearl has dropped three flowers on him, two on his waist-coat and one on his knee, which looks killed through the hole in his trousers. He gargles, and his mouth flabbers like a cow's underneath. He is like a death, but hasn't gone away altogether. You don't dare lift up the sacks like Patsy, although he is white and fascinating and full of don't touch. Mr. Loving there's a tramp under Pink Pearl, God has left a tramp under Pink Pearl.

Mr. Loving and Tom grunt him through the gates like furniture. He doesn't feel the nettles and one hand gets trodden on like a fish. He isn't going to die, so God needn't get ready to count him. Tom is laughing but Mr. Loving looks like he does when rats are in the potting-shed. He looks under Pink Pearl as though another death is there. Tom says he was the spitting image of Mr. Loving. So God must have loved the world and he made tramps in his image so they spit all the time. Mr. Loving must have been looking for truth under Pink Pearl if God said so.

You don't think he touched her
in any way
I've warned and warned her
But she's so young   No   no

But you never know
I said Never Never talk to strange men   and she
said something about cherry trees but wasn't it a
rhododendron   Loving said it was   I still think
    you
        should've
                called the Police   you never
                        Know

If you have a stick, I will give you one.
If you have not a stick
I will take it away from you.

We sit on sighing leather chairs with muscular
legs, and two have lions' feet clutching balls, and
two have eagles' feet doing the same. Up their
backs they have shining brown stretches, twisting
like seaweed.

When all the things are taken off, the table
becomes grim like dentists' waiting with groomed
wood in wreaths of polished sideways smoke patterns all over it, and it puts its feet down strongly
as though facing up to fight. When the tablecloth
is on, it looks like Church, and the white tablecloth

shines like faint sardines. It has flowers and leaves that whiten and turn like fish rising when the light catches it, but with no light they die back into the weave again, and are just thought there like pale blue.

The roses sit in their glass holes in the vase, and murmur in the afternoons of dark red sleeping over blue, smelling all over the room. Yellow roses are going to be a fine day with the lawn in lines, and white roses say Marriage slowly and quietly and smell of honeymoons in the room. The dark red ones lie in fat small cushions round the room, and love-in-the-mist says farewell in a frilled poem collar. Then they will turn over, and there will be petals like eyelids on the table. It happens when you're not there, but sometimes it happens when you're looking. Like soft hands clapping, there are petals in a rush and you have not been told this is going to happen. You can't think Stop, I will think petals falling, and there are. It is part of the sparrows and the toad under the mauve flowers, and the red maple branch that will touch the water whether or not you or God are watching and say it, like the gold and silves fishes lying under the water-lilies saying o, and stroking brown in the world going on. You can't say no fish when you see only the pink waterlilies, for they are like thinkings in spite of yourself thinking, and then there is a real yellow water-lily which stops all thinking.

God has started them all off, but some have gone on past him, and he must think how wonderful sometimes, seeing the golden fishes coming out of thinking and being golden fishes by themselves in front of him.

47

I'm so worried *about her. You worry too much,*
you know. All the time
Yes, yes, I know I do, but
You're right. I do   But   I don't know
We shall have to be watchful, Gee, Always. She's
got that look — Men look already
It is *worrying*
and the powder into all the wrinkles

On Sunday God sleeps after church, but everything goes on although the sparrows wait for him
to wake up for another seven days. Perhaps God
dreams a new world, not busy making stars and us
and having his rest, but dreaming all over again.
He may say that's no good it wouldn't work when
he wakes at four, or that's a good idea, we'll try it.
But being God he may have to be careful, as a dream
may be creating without him knowing. He may
have started off dreaming he was God and woken
up thinking that was a funny dream, but now I
must make a whale as I have a lot to do. If so, was
he God before he started dreaming, or did he dream
himself, hardening in to God later on, as he had no
father or mother which he arranged for his son
Jesus.

And if we're supposed to have God all through
us and be his spitting image, how do we know we're
not really God altogether, having forgotten the
dream and thinking now what did I make yesterday, which is why everything is so familiar and
unfamiliar.

It is very difficult as sometimes you feel like God, very happy and sad and thinking God's word Hallelujah, which he says on Sundays, and then you try and make something and you can't make a box properly, and how would you start on a whale. We can't really be God, because even if we grunt thinking we can't make a whale, but he wants us to be happy so he lets us make houses and chairs and aeroplanes, and keeps the whales and us for himself as only he knows the secret. It's a good thing for pondering, like Mary. He lets us be a god with a small 'g' to show us it's good to be like him, but never lets us make a graven image of him as it might begin all over again without him, and the devil might get hold of him then.

It would be very difficult to make a graven image of God, as it would have to be as big as the world, and completely gold. As he's everything, he could be a cloud or a horse or a gold elephant, but you're not allowed to label these God, and he was very strict about graven images of man and other people. He used forbidden in red.

You could get all the gold in the world together so that there wasn't any more left, and make a huge square going up and up, the biggest thing in the world, with GOD cut out of it so big everyone could read it. It would be very precious then, which would please him being gold and none left for men. The Egyptians should have done it, they came along first and they knew how to make pyramids, but everyone was so wicked that God was always smiting them, and they never got anything finished. Wonderful prophesies could have come out, and

49

no one ever prophets in the world now. No one says Verily very deep, or through trumpets, and It Came To Pass.

I have no peace of mind, pacify my mind.
Bring out your mind here before me, I shall
    pacify it.
It is impossible for me to bring out my mind.
Then I have pacified it.

There was a prophet once, asleep in a telephone box, not under Pink Pearl, and he woke up and ran out into all the traffic, and told them the kingdom was near and they must repent. But the policeman put him into a black lorry like a shiny zoo and they laughed, so they must have known he was a false prophet, and hidden him from the wrath which God would have sent to run him over as a judgement. This must be poetic justice, the judgement of prophets with long singing words and a blind Greek woman.

Three blind mice. Three blind mice. See how they run. Like the false prophet through the traffic. The farmer's wife caught them, not the policemen, and he wouldn't have a tail to cut off, but God might make them cut off his head in the black lorry, which is very clean, to stop him making poems.

The cars go very fast up and down the road, and once the devil lost one of his nine lives outside

the gate. They carried him under the oak tree with
don't look saying three times round the clover in
the lawn. They put sand over the oil and pink and
white bits and whispering brains, and the red looked
over-red on the black road, and fitted into the gaps,
and ran down like rain sticking the leaves together
and into the drain. It made you look because the
policeman stood over him and said poor devil a lot,
and it seemed amazing he could come again new
into the world, even as something else. His face
was very red and like a balloon with a face written
on it when you only blow it up a little. If he was
disguised as a human he had done it very well, but
the policeman seemed to have seen through him to
call him poor devil. Perhaps it was rather sad to
lose even one life for the devil, who hasn't a resurrection like us and is finished if he loses his ninth,
like the black cats.

Another policeman rode up on a thick white
horse, and the horse didn't like stepping on the red
which came up through the sand, lifting his legs
high. The policeman made him, and he jingled and
flashed all his harness and went over it very stiff
with his white neck pressed down, and the white
sailor's rope round it swinging. He left red horseshoes where he had crossed.

Whenever there is a dead or blood is out, it is
always Don't Look and Accident said like a red
snake dropping on a china plate, although looking
tells you. There is no need to don't touch, because
you only want to look. It is too terrible and deeply
unlucky for you to touch.

They take the devil away, and have covered his

51

red face with the policeman's handkerchief, which he puts down on it like a picnic, but it comes through that as well as the sand. Evil rubs off onto people the vicar says, so it must from the devil's face, and the policeman won't want his handkerchief back even if they wash it. When Jesus bled he was free of stain, so evil couldn't rub off as he never had any. No one got red off him, even the man with the spear.

Mr. Loving asks Tom to take a bucket of water and wash the lawn under the oak. His face is very white and his eyes must be weak for looking at red, as he says he cannot stand the sight of blood. After Tom has gone there are still bits left on the clover if you look. There is a smell of iron there. Perhaps the oak tree will become very large now it has been redeemed, for they say we are much better as Jesus redeemed us when he used his blood for it. This must be right, which is when happenings come together holding hands with sight and truth, and truth is knowing the right. The oak is king of the trees and Jesus was king of men, so both can be redeemed by blood, and the acorns are the children of the oak and we are the children of men. So it all goes on happening right. You would think there would have to be for it all at least one whole sea, but such a little seems to do for redeeming things. The only thing is, does the devil's blood redeem. No one has said. But if he is disguised, then he has to have his own blood, so it must work. Redeem then is a green word, all over the clover. They call the white lorry an ambulance, which is a lovely word suiting the time when the owls come out better than a white lorry. It is a dark yellow word, like the dusk making the eyes wide with owls, and trying to see mystery which is dark blue. Ambulance is the light left in the earth's thinking when the dusk is over everything, covering the trees' faces, and mystery is quiet and pins stars onto your pricked face when you look up. People don't seem to see the coloured words which ring. And some suit other names better. Deliver is written on the serpent's back, slithering up God's special tree, Herbacious pulls an A through long grass like a grazing cow, Charity is a white cat with her paws together, and Integrity grinds its horse's bit. Words need us, though, and reading hammers them like black pegs through the eyes and into your head so deep that the ears hear them, but birds sing all the no words, and streams run away with lots of no words past us, leaving them no time to get stuck in the ears like goose grass, and to go on round the mind knocking like red apples.

And horses need no words when they are together. They don't think Flies in black, and stand back looking at Flies in black, but nod whisking, because they're horses.

Grownups seem to have been born again past being children, as they don't see, standing with umbrellas keeping off misunderstanding which rains through the trees, and tangled up in words and time and cooking and the news. And horses being horses right along their ears as they look. Please is a word for cats' backs, and No is down dogs' ears. All day the sun spreads the breadfull of meadows with buttercups, and we eat strawberries like old bishops' noses, with cream saying a pulled-out glop. Cream winds yellow arms round nestling, satisfied with being cream. The sun creams the butter-coats of the cows, the moo coming out of their eyes first in roundness. Their brown eyelashes pat the growing moo, and they hush the hot sun when he walks into the shadows where they lie like baths. And happiness sits on the branches with all the green leaves saying cows and buttercups, sky and cats washing legs, eggs, and bees with orange tails.

The grownups say happiness in black, holding it like birds too tight, and then forget happiness, and it goes away from the grownups over the grass and through the daisies, and sometimes it goes by on the red bus on the white road under the heavy, hanging green elm trees, making dust.

      o don't look
              look away
                    that poor
dog there   *hurry away don't look*   *o some beast*
must've left it the
    poor
    poor
    thing.   *and just after that other*
    awful accident
last week
        who was he Gee
O
someyoungidiot on a motorbike here it
                   is

Patrick Fallon of 15 Parkland Lane was killed last
night when the motorcycle he was riding crashed
into a wall at the corner of Beechmount Road and
The Avenue. It is thought the accident was caused
by mud on the road from the lorries using Homelea
gravel pits. Mr. Fallon, who was 18, was due to
marry Miss Sheila Cox, also of Parklands Lane, on
May 20th. At the inquest sympathy was extended
h'mmm her   etcetera   etcetera
   Yes there you are   young idiot
threw *his life away   ah Gee*
pity . . . poor lad   itsawful
   all young
         idiots
  Couldn't have been the mud
    its all dust there now

> *Since in reality all is void*
> *whereon can the dust fall?*

Sadness can sit on a corner of the tablecloth
under the tulip tree, and no one knows why it
comes and why it is sadness. It can even be inside
a cake, looking in the jam. Sadness smells of rain
and the garden seat whose wood is grey like the
hairs of some horses, and wrings its hands on the
backs of white iron chairs with the tea in a silver
teapot like the Shah of Persia, and the new vicar
eating round a scone like a rat gnawing a hole.

Sadness comes under a chestnut tree, looking up, and a tiny amen for a wren. It can stay all night on a blue square on the bedspread, while happiness goes to sleep in pink, with yellow roses. It can say S unbearably in a black, hairy dog curled to sleep on a short chain, with his nose hidden away from it in his fur. You cannot look at it in monkeys' eyes for it hurts them looking back. It is sometimes o dear and a stiff heart, but it can be long and thin like trying to see Greece too far back. Music can bring it running like lost lions, like Adam crying Jehovah, and pineapple you with fear as well, and it can fall into the white part of icecream and completely die in the chocolate, with happiness in the pink between. It is death of course, too, and wet rabbits in hutches. And grownups eat it like spinach, feeling it hard and stitched like cricket balls.

It hurts itself on the red bus too, in an empty seat and in a bunch of flowers, and gets very big and slow for a dead king. Mostly it is in men, for animals carry it with them for us to feel for them, and it is worst for cold children and old dogs.

Mother says we will go up to see Mrs. Browning's puppies at the farm. She is wearing long beads with a pearl in between glass rods, looped round like spare reins on the coalman's horse. She says, Let's go over the Enchanted Meadow, and see if we can see any Fairies in the Wood. It's silly and you feel hedgehogs.

We go past the cherry trees and the old apple tree with its chin on the ground, where a single bee comes and goes from a small hole in the earth, and as we open the old faded iron gate the orchard and the kitchen garden look at each other. As we close it with a click, like bats snicking, the kitchen garden jumps like soldiers. The lettuces frill away up to the brick wall which smells of the days which the sun has led along it, like children with mothers, and there are gaps where Mr. Loving has cut some, with sadness unexpectedly in the grins of bare earth. Some have gone past Mr. Loving and the basket on legs, green rockets peppered at the top with triumph, like Jack and the Beanstalk. Pink and mauve colombines play at queens in a corner because Mother said o leave them and the dark bronze cabbages breath up to them like carp. Some cabbages hold a jewel of rain in their turbans like rajahs. They march, and sit one step between marching. Along the wall, peaches and apples are stretched and nailed with spreading wood like Jesus, his head like the thorn hedge plaited round Mr. Browning's farm.

Fairies oh of course *I've seen them*
                    yes
Of course *I want you to be Happy   to be*
      happy
                    Happy Birthday ! Happy
   Christmas !   New Year   God is Happy for us
I am happy   are you happy
Come says the Mother in the Story Book   Come let
us run and be Happy
   No I can't run
      I'm out of breath   no   no

you mustn't be sad *Deffy*
> *Sad is bad*
> *Sad is mad*
> *Allahabad Deffy is where they race the*
Akhal Teke golden horses   O Uncle Ormonde   hur-
ray   hurray   I shouldn't leave that wet umbrella
in there, Ormonde —
> *Oh it's very sad, Mrs. Johnson. Terribly sad   and*
she's so young
>> *six of those*
>> *cream ones*
>>> *please*
>> *oh how sad*
>>> *yes those*
>>> *please*

Tom's weeding in the softness of carrots, and his
back has a line down under his blue shirt like Mr.
Browning's fat bull. He says good morning to
Mother quickly, keeping the carrots in his eyes. He
carries seed packets in his back pockets and sniffs
in jerks down the string lines writing seeds down.
When he has covered them, he walks up and down
in rhinocerous boots, and then he will stand twisted
against his rake like ivy growing. His hands have
stopped being hands, like dogs begging over the
top of the rake, and he stands thinking turnips and
carrots into the lines with the sun looking down on
his eyebrows.

Tom's hair smells of the chocolate sheep in Mr.
Browning's white flock, and where he goes he

leaves badger behind in patches. Mr. Loving doesn't plant and weed with his boots looking sad and forgotten behind, kneeling like withered black pigs, and with the nails spelling silver full-stops with a little horse-shoe heel. He tells Tom to weed or frown the lawn, and sweep the leaves that run away.

Tom can pick up broody hens, holding them flat like fruit cake, their legs stiff and waiting for sitting again. He mixes their food, chalking it over his shirt, stirring it with a porridged hand.

Mr. Loving womans among the roses, and always has green string and straw-manes in his apron pocket. He holds the grapes as though fitting them like light bulbs, but when he has cut them they say oh many times like a bunch of firm sea, or plum pugs' eyes, with their own stalk T for Mr. Loving to carry them. He spoons in rows of flat boxes, and childrens the hair of new plants, smiling like a dead rat. He doesn't hit the walnut tree, but the angel doesn't like him and reads hard. He fits white bags over the big pears like Mrs. Loving stepping into a stocking he was holding one day, when you shouldn't look.

He strokes the pears like he smoothed down the horse's nose of Mrs. Loving's white leg, slowly. The pears look like beneath the white bull at the show, but you mustn't say. The bull walks pear-heavy in the sun, swinging his pyjama tail and stringing ff's from his gleaming nose. His grocer processioned him on a chained stick like a coronation.

Now we're in the Enchanted Field we may see the Fairies, says Mother. She hasn't seen the old tortoise planked into his waistcoat like a boat,

59

rowing along the wall. He steps at a lettuce and
eats, saying a pink glum. If he sees you he sighs
back into old leather.

Ar, Oi seen a thing or two
An' Miss Deffy done too
Dirty ol' bugger, that's what.
An' 'e a churchwarden an' all — Gawd
Bad as the ol' bugger up the road what do fancy
lil boys

And, mingling with truth among the flowers,
I have forgotten what to say.

It is very hot in the field, with lace umbrella
flowers and snapdragons which pinch their cheeks
like pekinese barks. Mother says Fairies to please,
but fairies are wild and have gone, as they cannot
stand the iron we have in our days. They have left
their feeling in the pine trees, and where are ferns
and moss. Their feeling looks round at you like
foxes from the pine trees, and is sad with a long
going away on the downs where the wind canters
over the hare-bells and scabious, and strokes the
angry orange hares. They leave their old feeling,
and only pretend sees them, for they have closed
the doors of the hills, and told the mushrooms to

Remember, with smoke and brown leaves and a long goodbye.

We go through the pines and into Mr. Browning's field, which has been told to make corn like the Israelites coming.

Mrs. Browning is in daisies all over, and There now. Her feet slipper in old squirrel tails, and her arms are fat rhubarb out of the wrinkled daisies. She matresses down the front, but her legs are marbled blue and white, very unlucky, like the white under flatfish. She has two patched cats that sit on the sides like lords' gateways, on her windowsill.

The puppies are like new slippers, buttered, with pincushion faces. Suddenly Mrs. Browning's sad, sideways slippers look like old, leftover pekinese. O Mam, the old billygoat died. Mother says oh like an old dog sitting down. He carried bits of the sky around on his horns, and aired the morning on them like a blue sheet. He said Heh like a very old man and coughed, slapping his ears. He looked at you very light and old, with Egyptian eyes. He wore himself high in his rug, and was another disguise for the devil to come into, being the prince of darkness all through the night, popping stars with his horns and pointing with his tongue, which is rude in us. He was so old he really welcomed death said Mrs. Browning. Hello, Billy Death. We had to take his horns off, to get him down deep enough. Very deep and back near hell so the devil can't use him again up here. We had to cut the horns off Billy Death, and the devil wears them now instead.

We are taken to see the father Bull. Tom takes

our brown cow crossing sideways on a halter, to grow a calf from him. He is sitting like a pulled-up boat, very heavy into the ground on his anchor-chain. He has a little field with buttercups, and has folded his deckchair knees away. He chews his thoughts which say Hot Bull, and his ears telephone Bull to us. His tail skips with itself, and he moons his head round on to his back, throwing the chain up like a row of silves fishes. Flies pin on his skin, and he bothers with little rubbery shakes tossing an F at them through his clenched nose.

Mrs. Browning calls him her baby, and he tele-phones Bull back to her like the King saying Hello. Here they come, says Mrs. Browning, and the Bull turns his head and Cows grapefruit into his eyes. They are coming across his field for milking. He says a long moo down his hose throat, looking all Cow. He gets up, leaning himself into standing, and stretches bull back all over into himself with his tail roping a handle. Then he opens his mouth as though water is coming out, but he has a small thunderstorm deep inside him instead. The cows don't look Bull back at him, they walk past thinking all cow and good stomachs. Mrs. Browning says Hello Bill, and bends down oh dear, to pull the chain up. He knits it in shining O's over his arm, and the Bull swings behind, rowing his fat brown through the buttercups like the tortoise, one two and his feet pointing heavy sadness. He takes his horns in through the cowshed carefully, like a ladder.

He was my Baby, says Mrs. Browning. Once Mr. Browning called her old cow when you shouldn't be listening coming for butter, so perhaps he is really half a bull like Greece, and eats children, which is why Mrs. Browning says he is very fond of children, like bacon.

You don't really think so, but perhaps that is why Mrs. Browning hasn't had any real children at all because her bull Baby would have taken such a lot of growing up. It would have been better if Mr. Browning had been half a Greek horse, and then they could have had a foal, which is nicer. Then Mrs. Browning wouldn't be so sad when she says he is my Baby. But Mr. Browning has never called her old horse so she couldn't. You came adopted, so no one said she was my baby being happy or sad saying it. She is *my* Baby, *saying* it.

Do you think it's wise to let her see — I mean everything?

Very coarse people, I mean he never waited till we'd gone. And the poor cow fell down, right on to her knees, that awful bull was so heavy. *I'm sure it's not kind . . . ? And do you know,*

He laughed. *The wife's odd, no* children.
just

Deffy stared and stared at her, and at the er the . . . bull, wouldn't shake hands, just kept back *all the time*

        honestly

The Cow and the Man both gone out of sight.

63

And Rosemary comes to tea. Show her the garden and your toys. Rosemary wants a chow dog for her own with polar bear's eyes and a black tongue like the devil. Uncle has brought O'Leary to stay, he carries his hair on his bones stiffly, like a clothes horse, and feels his corners. The biggest breed of dog in the world, says Uncle. You can smoothe his breed over his thatched nose and his bumped eyebrows like marsh humps with long grass, and his yellow eyes look at the King of Ireland, nearly to Greece with his long look. Sadness walks with his big knees except when he runs in the field, hooking his tail with running, swallowing over the field like a jerked rug, pronging himself down like a fork in front, hair and eyes and off again. He lifts his lip when he comes, his head sideways, his tail holding a low G. One tooth says milk and pillar, and his back mountain-teeth shine out of the pink and black newts' fin down the sides of his mouth. His ears are surprised they are O'Leary. He lies down like a slung grey net over the stones. He is devoted, mother says, which is laid on his dog's heart altar like red velvet, when his tail flicks S on the gravel. When he is going to say M he licks you instead. You love O'Leary full of big love like holding an ostrich egg of warm loves. Rosemary is afraid of him and her fair hair is silly, of course he won't bite. Chows have black tongues which is rude, and they frown with Bear which is sleepy and dangerous. Take Rosemary out to see the garden. She says the maples aren't Japanese, they come from Canada. The maples say Japan like birds' writing. You know. They say there, and look, with their hands, and the waterlilies have Japan in yellow sneezes in the middle of their pink holders. The water goes through brown Japan and through into thinking, and Japan takes orange and white, and paints gold and silver into the fish shine. Japan says, in all colours, everything you want to say, but like a bell. Canada is up and down like dogs' teeth, and is sad with lakes, like everlasting.

But
  Ormonde
   Gypsies!
May — it's an experiment I knew both father and mother salt of the earth both of them No need to worry there's no bad blood
   There
   My God I'm catching a cold well
 wheres   my Girl
Give her a pony May No wait I'll take her up to Little Egypt in August now don't fuss My God how you fuss how Gerald stands you I don't know can't imagine Now Ah my little Defiance now May don't start like that like my Nearco mare all mad you know bloody well what her name is Deffy! Love! But my God she's going to break some hearts one day eh my love. Deffy I've got a Celestial listen Celestial Horse for you to ride only if you can ride him mind horse for a Prince Deffy or a Princess oh he's golden all over, all over like plated gold my handsome little Deffy

65

and a
black
Mongolian

eye !
All for you   May did you know Chinese
emperors fought over him a thousand years ago
huh   silly cows gone
*   a thousand ages in their sight are like an Evening*
Gone   isn't that it Deffy   a thousand gold pieces
for one golden Ferghana stallion   and just for
you
Now let's unpack. Poor old O'Leary hello you hell-
hound you   open the door   ahh always bloody
stiff   oh aha   aha   he's flattened her   that's 15
stone of All Dog Deffy. look at him go   alright
love?   Thatsa girl   Go on May what's a lawn for
Here goood dog ah thats my goooooooood dog and
you're my lovely girl too Deffy like a pup from him
would you call him Ard Ri now the High King   Aha
here's Margaret still a virgin then Maggie   My God
I have got a cold   Fuck

Rosemary says, My eyes are blue. Yours are green,
like grass. No one likes green eyes. Horses do,
horses and cows love green eyes. Blue is common,
said like rough grasshopper legs and one church bell.
   Delegation is a word from the news. It turns
like a shilling on a table. Delegation, you say.
Rosemary is like a canary. Soft-yellow. You don't
understand. You *see* each other. Understand walks

66

one-two-three-four, like a black bull pushing with his chest. *Te-ea.* Come indoors now and wash your hands.

Rosemary has the blue soap. I love blue. You could bite yellow. And your dog smells. Enormity you've heard in talking. An enormity squats under the sideboard with a mahogany trunk, breathing. Blasphemy is Jesus Christ, said like a black donkey. Jesus one half hasn't any butter, Christ is buttered and with jam. Blasphemy creams out of the sides, and salvation is in the middle. You whisper it like the serpents oiling through Eve's tree. God won't suspect it being blasphemy if it's said into a dry scone, without butter. She ought to have her head cut off and you could hide it in the larder, on a blue country plate. With all her hair plaited around it like a pastry.

Even other dogs don't like chows. You know she is kicking O'Leary, who is carpeted under the table, with her special shiny dog's-nose dancing shoes. She reaches out for a cake, pretending to slip so that she can kick him harder. He yelps. Oh poor dog, is your dog under the table. Your heart pinches like a hot-cross-bun, and your throat is crumbed with stuffed toads.

He martyrs out from under the tablecloth and sits beside you, his nose saying Cakes sideways, in red cherried letters and half-green licks. His eyes politely don't look, on purpose. He sits like a Russian with his beard very high over your teacup, and with his feet a long straight down. He sighs and looks pinned into clear yellow out of the window to the King of Ireland.

Afterwards we sit on a bank, and the grass is dry and hedgehogs under the knees. I've seen your garden and your trees which come from Canada and not Japan at all.

She hasn't seen the Horse Prince. He might oracle on her. First you must bring him something, although he doesn't always eat. But you can leave yourself there for the night, which is fortune and mystery both of which night carries in a purple bag, leaving them smelling like the yellow mushrooms under the cedar tree, and shining like apricots.

Cook nearly catches. What are you two up to. A drink of milk, it's so cool in the larder. He may not eat marmalade, but it is a gift like the three kings, and it makes ice and orange into a shine like a soft sun, with goldfish pieces stopped in it.

The rhododendrons are rusty, where their branches step in slow snakes and wind up like Buddha's in and out arms. It is dark and calm, with a knowing of leaves and earth under them. Why do you call him the Horse Prince. He just is. If you are still, stay still; he may utter an oracle. They cut his head off, and he says oracles. The head has bursting glass eyes, and a red mouth round the teeth which grip on Ha Ha like limpets. There are saucers and jars on the dead leaves around him, and all the food has gone. It smells of damp prophecies and white toadstools like witches' eggs. One day the Horse Prince, who was not quite as far off as Greece, will say Terrible, Terrible, in a brass voice. His Name is Jericho. He will tell and foretell when the world will roll up like a hedgehog and carry the sea away stuck on his back, into the time past all Amens. Who shall I marry? But he is gagged into a red U with his sonata teeth ready. He still has the apple on a cabbage leaf. Something small has been eating them. It's silly. Rosemary is crouching in her pink dress. Her socks are long and white, like a calf's, and she has cutlet knickers. Her fair hair shall have a burnt offering. The matches are damp, so the marmalade will run and slide and mess, aha and aha. You pat a statue on her and she doesn't believe. Her blue eyes are empty of I believe, even of I hate you or O heavens. Then she wails like a kitten under the lid on Mr. Loving's bucket. She must bow down and idolise, or you will get her to play ropes in the cowshed and see, like this. Now I hate you, said like a tom cat with whiting bone whiskers.

Give her your other teddy. You don't need two. You cling drowning in want for the button eyes. You mustn't be selfish, said like a snail under a shoe. Please God send down tootache, ear ache and no holes so she'll die like a paper bag or strangling on a line of socks. Unmentionable can be said going thin through a mangle, and Disaster ladles after her down the hall like a bloodhound. Hot found out, always found out. She may have upset an oracle, or an ability. Ability jumps over the hedge like a piebald goat with his tail fanning. The mothers talk on like bees, legging over the clover words, humming with talk like the hornet news. Bees don't say Bees, or a nice day, or just two brown, please, and the rest going up round the chimneys and saying flat, flat on the ivy. Bees *are* Bees.

If only she was
        like
the little Dodds' child
            such a nice
            child
    I hope there's no viciousness there, Gee
            Oh lord no
                        no
    We've all pulled the wings off flies   May
            if we're honest
    I've seen Rosemary's brother myself
            many times   Rosemary's brother?
    Yes   yes here in the dining room   when?
    Oh   after that last party when was it
            or was it a butterfly

        A butterfly
            Asleep, perched upon
            the temple bell.

In the cowshed, Tom brings in Dolly and Jersey
for their milk. They bring bits of field and buttercups, and maps of brown and white seas. They put
their feet so and so on the path, and beat their sides
with carpet tails. Tom opens the gates, and they go
through looking low at him like old men on sticks.
Dolly has had a calf, and she is bursting like a
wind-cherub, but Jersey is loose like gathered blankets and a next-day balloon. Tom bracelets their

necks with the heavy ringing chains, and they iron their chins round the stone trough after their diced cake, leaving wet like snails. They're good cows, Tom says. They look round good, like people with behaviour. They lick their noses with goose-grass tongues. Tom has yellow dog soap and a small silver bucket, washing his hands and arms like a fly polishing. He puts his hand onto their backs and washes them underneath like flannelling faces. On one finger he has a gold belt ring like a mouse's dog collar. They must have clean udders. Udder is a rude word, says Rosemary. Not half as rude as some I do know. Tom butts the cow deep in her side, and the milk pings. Tell us. A rude word, a really rude word, Tom. Oh Please. His fingers feel the milk out. Adder, then. Adder isn't rude. It's a snake. You two young ladies don't want to know rude words. Two nice young ladies like you. We're not nice, we're horrible. Horrible is a word with running black legs into corners. Don't know any. Oh, you liar, Tom. Bloody's one, but that's not very bad. Come on, a really awful one. Like Thunderstruck sounds. It's funny how a word can be bad from a good. Malediction and Manifest are twins. Who first said it should be bad. Perhaps they slid apart off the devil's forked tongue. God says Everlasting and Evermore, and Verily, which wags its curly tail. The Holy Ghost says Amen and Tomb, three times like an iron door. The devil says Disaster like a trayful of black teacups, and Asp like a hot horse-shoe going into water. Sometimes he has a headache and says Zebra backwards across his forehead. Pots bark and windows say goodbye to passing horses.

71

Exquisite embroiders itself, and Comfort goes to sleep in fur. Horses stand saying a long Doom to each other when thunder is coming like Someone with a mask on, running like pylons. Final hangs itself up like a soft, stretched bucket on a long red nail, and once the day hit its knees with you with a racquet under the tented chestnut, until it turned into hay and it was time to sleep with the windows open. The day said o dear, it's quick night. The Holy Ghost sat on one of the flower candles on the chestnut tree, and the tree said *Mind*. Because of the thunder halfway up the stairs. But it was alright because the big cake said Majesty to everyone, with cream and red safety on its head, and green hellos. Nothing can happen when there is a big cake saying Me, born into the world of men like Hundreds and Thousands. Me saying me, and the cake saying me, too.

Tom's hands shape and pull the milk out. Jersey has friendly bananas and squashes pinging like Sundays pillows. Dolly has small thumbs and rains milk while waiting for Tom. Her legs bend out with pushing milk like paddling fat women. He can't handful them, and pianos them wetly instead, like sausages with mouths. She gives so much milk it thumps and plups into hushing froth, like drowning noise in custard. The calf stayed with her, its mouth wanting, saying thok with its head, like coming up under a blanket on the line. Its glass nose shapes Mat which is a square word, blinked at.

Go back to the house now, Tom said, all red and pulling it on handcutting string, when it went away to be veal in the lorry. Veal is tearful like babies wrapped in paper, like pink eyes and lampshade ears on jellied plates. Tom says stop teasing, you're young ladies. Ladies is a pink vest word, like peaches with lace tops, but when Tom says it with teeth, it is brown with jackdaw eyes and gives you cat strokings down your front. Tom's hair goes fingering round at the back of his head, like a cow's star hair on her face.

It is all very strange, very sudden. Sudden jumps twice like flinging down a dead rabbit. The horns and Tom's hair and Rosemary's dress with yellow squares, and all our feet come into the eyes, and go out again like one after the other people in a procession. You can put the nose and the horns and the eyes and the neck, the long tail and the coconut feet, one by one just like that. And put them together into a sudden Cow. They can't be anything else. You can't say altogether: And this is Tom. Only magic does that, for princesses mostly, but you can put Tom together from your careful pieces of looking. And Rosemary, and the sad ground. But you can only put yourself quite together in the mirror, and that is only what other people see. Cows see you nicely, and all animals put you into a real piece. It is difficult, as bits stay in the grass, and a long way up trees, and on a dog's nose. And bits fly off with the birds and the wind. Very difficult for all yourself to stay with you, even when you look in the mirror and say Real Me, like a big cake. What oh what is the *Me*, and what is only the looking, like being glass inside and out. When does it change and you say ah *me*, without taking the cherries off and leaving holes, and you can laugh with knowing *me*. Like gypsies and captains, and Indians from the big ships who bend round you like giving sweets to deer. They're very beautiful and forbidden, with black hair and tomato lips and they don't smell like Tom, but like the three kings. They wear silver chains round their wrists, which have mauve grapeskins over their green flesh, and have teeth for apples. They have real eyes for knowing through looking behind afterwards, full of beautiful cat strokings, and black swans. Missy they say, like calling cats, and they wave goodbye under the trees like holding up parrots to see. They are people like Tom and Rosemary and mother, and all saying me and not me. Sometimes you aren't put in, and are not me forever, but half, like Eddy. They say it's not his fault and that God didn't go wrong either. He can't look and he sees nothing, only stares very hard at no spiders. He doesn't even see a not me, and he isn't an animal even, to look back over itself. You knock up against looking at him, and feel don't touch like the dead. You must feel sorry for him, but he isn't O Poor, Poor like an animal; you can't feel O for him as they say. He's keep back, like not quite dead, and white. They say God feels sorry, but he must have made him first. Perhaps God didn't put the me in right, just this once, without thinking it properly. God has to think to get it all right, and think the me hard into you as he makes you. And then he leaves it to you to find what sort of me he put in, like a puppy over bones, growling. Like hide and seek years. But sometimes you know, right from the start. The me is *hard* me and in tight, but still some

74

pieces get left on foxgloves, and are cold at night, and get tight when the moon pulls, even though they are still the whole me. You don't know if it's your fault or God's fault. Even the mirror which looks me all together in one piece, even then the me says o dear into the eyes, like God worried. The grownups hold themselves in their me like jugs, and are very tidy. They don't leave their bits on dandelions or feeling lost mothers on the stars, but sometimes they let a small not-me sit out on a long stare. But the stare doesn't see either the not-me or their own special me. They say Life to each other very often, thinking brown. Life climbs a stalk in a red and yellow jacket, and says hello at the top with hoopla feet, and is a green plum going red on a wall. It isn't wasps and never has been pencils.

When the mosquito jabs at a lump of iron,
Nothing is left to you at this moment
But to burst into a loud laugh.

Yere
    What's ee got on under thic purty dress then
    Miss Deffy
    Don't ee like Tom then   eh   eh now

Harr moi yand der goo in a lotta queer places now
    don't it, moi dear

75

An me cock
An me ol' cock   which cock she says   Gor
bless er
Why thic little old bantam cock what oi der yave
at 'ome moi dear

Yere
Gie us a Kiss then   Kiss ol' Tom goodbye
*   not a word   moind*
Not a word now   Miss Deffy
                        Willyer
                            eh

Life says ah with two chord voices when there are roses, and looks back to brown birds under the green leaves, and sleeps with pigeons, and says Nineveh where there are streams which hold bits of me and peoples' dropped not-me. Even when the people are all dead, life will go over them with a sack and shoes in the grass, where there are no cowpats or dandelions allowed.

The cows take the evening into the lower meadow, and Tea rings a brass Indian bell round an elephant and a tiger and the two long-tailed birds. Under its skirts, the teapot has leaves like thoughts which are caught whirling in the strainer, except one which runs round the cup like a shrimp in a netted pool. It is tall and dark. They laugh. Like a deep policeman, the teapot says I am a Teapot, and takes your face round it and over the knots, and bloodhounds it down the arches and runs it up the spout into a point of nothing. If you smile, teeth are said and eyes soldier in the spaces, up down. You'll stay like it, caught on the silver with teeth and eyes and ooo and eee.

Father chases and catches music after tea, and the grown ups look not-me over the piano, meaning it. You see seals in caves and a dead lady on a green sofa, and the sun shakes the evening on the lawn's hand. Music goes like ginger terriers, cats on a fence, or whales enjoying the sea, with black towers and white girls when they are maidens. It pours all the not-me into a green bottle with bubbles in the glass, and amber sometimes and amethyst, but still with bubbles. Music runs with a red string round all the begonias long before they went to war, and ends in forever and ever or happily ever after, which is different. When God finishes anything very big he plays elephant music on his organ, decorated with golden hallelujahs, turning red and blue with countenance. Bigger than Whales, he made Beethoven for ending dinosaurs, and the Garden of Eden when it rained early on and he thought of sunshine for Adam and Eve. And we are descended in steps from Adam and Eve in our bath, leaving the chimpanzees sitting in their original. And always there were sparrows. God thought of water first, which came easily, but the land and the stars hurt to think into making hard, and he liked making the animals best. Adam and Eve worried him at the end of the week. A mouse came into the prelude once, and father hit it with the walking stick. It tried to climb slowly, on its back, as he picked it up. Like interrupting cook with scrambled eggs, it

77

came in the middle of the prelude and father said damn, like stings. He threw it out of the front door, and you went to look. But its life came back and it washed its hands, screaming with red teeth and gravel in one eye. Quickly. Oh Gerald you should have. Oh quickly. Oh the poor little thing, and she's seen.

When God had made everything and rested, he must have said O damn I've forgotten the mice, and had to get up again. So no one likes mice, especially God, who put making traps into peoples' minds, and he never says anything to them when they arrive in heaven, although he suffers with sparrows, and Jesus likes robins best. Mice are always frightened of the seventh day and God full of pudding before he put newspapers into people.

We'll all go to the circus. It's coming soon. Please God make it a fine day and forget it says pomp and circumstance in red and yellow with tigers and vanity lit up. Please God, and I'll be good, and I promise I didn't see the mouse if you didn't like it. I'll take the mouse out of my mind for you, but I'm sorry I can't take out the circus even for Jesus sake, Amen.

When you know that what you need
Is not the snare nor the net,
But the hare and the fish . . .

Can't you find anything useful to do?
Can't you find anything to do?
Can't you find . . .
Can't you   you   Can't

First edition! I say Gerald
m'mm rather fine aren't they
No dear   Deffy   we don't touch them
they're very   special
Ah this key's stiff   well you can't have
kid's paws all over them
What do you think of these then   h'm?   Eh?
              Aha

Sunday is for horses with chained bible harness. Keep your hand flat, or you won't get the gift of tongues. Little children shall suffer the sheep from the goats, and the cow's in the corn on the Sabbath Day.

Things happen like flowers to us. One day happens like a bead. It can be any colour and the days are on a string, and then you have a birthday, which makes the necklace. And you are still you, and there are still molehills and jam, and black tar, and rain raining on the stones. And days run, making you. And mice are sharpened for running through their days, not blunt for the sunt to sit on.

One night a mouse came up on the table and drank from the bedtime cup. He held on with help feet, and his tail questioned. Then he sat up and reproved himself while praying under his whiskers.

His bead had rolled him into a mouse for a year, not like you going on until white hair and God at the end.

It rains on the stones. When you're inside, breathing knife-smells off the glass, it ticks with a stopped time, and a bird has a bath where a stone has left room. It leaves secrets on moss, and resurrection in the spaces between Here Lies. Ferns ring bells silently with drops, but people look long noses. Letters come at Christmas, bat-handed by wet postmen, and cows do cowpats with rain knitting wet strings all down them. Outside it rains on the world, and you think with the religious earth caring for primroses. The earth thinks back under rain, but you think time. Only winter tea's lights can kill time when it hurts with rain, and has unknitted you from the world, which goes on even in the dark, like Assyrians. It is sad with tearful wet wool, and the cock looks out from the little door with no thank you down his green feathers, and his red hat annoyed quickly. One hen stands so wet that she can't tell you anything but wet hen, standing. Wet dogs look Moses all over before they shake, and have ended hysterics in their tails which puts them right. They taste their noses, and do long icecreams under their legs until it annoys Father. Stop it or out, but they can't ever, and look Moses worse. Dogs are vulgar, said like plops in the lavatory.

The angel has gone. He never reads in the rain, even in summer. He only comes when summer becomes special, smelling of grey sea and oily knives and hay when it's asleep and not grass. The wind is very wide then with kindness, and the world hums in green and yellow with horse patterns. In winter the wind narrows and eyes everything like a thin grey cat, leaving ice for fishes' windows. When the sky knocks, and white waits behind the world like a bear shaking its head, then it will snow. It talks snow through its teeth, leaving people cut out in black and fever all over the morning, too bright. At night the snow walks over the world like a white camel with no feet showing. Robins leave blood behind on the snow, and in the sun a tree has cried all over it like a dropped alphabet, and like sinners. Repentence is snow sugaring up and along, and up and along, and up and along a fence with a silver birch downhill where forgiveness is blue and clear in the cold shadows. Pine trees remember very hard in winter and brush regrets out of the sky, and the wood makes room for badgers. Sometimes it's all perfect, as though God had set it out right and came along and iced it with perfection with nothing wrong anywhere. Sometimes God made it *just* not right. A tree or a field isn't quite right, and you can't do anything about it, however hard you try thinking, or saying it is alright really, God. God knows you're telling a lie to please him. It has to be both of you together, seeing it, and saying Perfection like warm old men, and some things aren't even by God, they've done it themselves. And then you and God meet it together and Agreement is all over God's face, like a golden clock with special letters like careful spiders. God isn't angry at all, because it took on Perfection before he told us to look and care. Stars are like this, and the feelings that web some places with regrets, and nature like an eiderdown on God's bed. Rocks and some parts of sky, and night and ponds do it too. But God leaves some ponds out, and they go back and back until they reach into a black forever. People are unhappy at these ponds. God sends Gabriel to people sometimes, he flies very soft like an owl, and has been given big eyes like God's spectacles to see into souls' corners. Even though he gets run into sometimes he goes on, being everlasting like the devil. Nothing ever happens to Father Christmas. Gabriel takes messages, getting his wings through doorways and telling the Virgin she was lucky. He says All Hail, and his feet never get cold flying as he doesn't come Father Christmas' way. He Announces tidings like the news in a very meet so to do voice and his hands going Our Father. White lilies tell the Virgin too about coffins, and tell everyone to get married to the Church at Easter.

Some flowers go Pardon all down into mauve, and some do very straight sums up and down with their leaves. There are peaches with amazed branches against the wall like Jesus. Rather like Jesus. Rather is a word panting like a hot dog looking at you in summer when he can't run. Peaches smell like our arms held up to the sun, when you watch the hairs as near as near as insect eyes. You can look into grass like that too, but the sun must be there, and flies flying.

I wish she wouldn't talk to all those men. *Strange* men.

With every gust of wind
the butterfly changes its place
on the willow.

Strange men   strange men
talking   talking to
            strange me

On the mushroom
Is stuck the leaf
of some unknown tree.

How it hurts. You can't sit and say good, good. It is like thank you, meant. One day you will be able to sit and say it and you will be knitted into all the you, and no difficulties, and where eggs come from really. And do orders for being grown up. Hello, and appointments, and some bacon, and don't to people. And you say I, and it stands there looking at you like an elephant. Now you say I, but it says You, back. It doesn't want to be bothered yet, though not hairy like Cook's bother.

Sometimes it hurts being you and everyone. It hurts all over the sun and the world being wonderful, and the trees all hurt so much with truly thankful, Amen. Like Amen to the moon sometimes, when the stars go into your head, and Uttermost is said like a black and white bird flying up into a tree with a long tail. A Perfection sometimes comes like this too, with God or without, like sleeves without stitches in a red coat. It is different to thankyou on birthdays, which aren't so filling. Thank you, thanks, comes from horseshoes at the blacksmith. One horse is varnished in the doorway, its tail very tidy for being so big. He turns his bridle which blocks him into a horse, and marbles his lips, and at the back he is all bottled out, and gloved into rolls and divides like brown waves that have stopped and gone smelling into conkers. He is another perfection, made like a velvet blanket round you.

When Cook puts feathers on the fire it smells of the blacksmith and makes you think of another horse, with colours like meat in jelly, in glass, and pink tombstones, who brings the coal and stands on high bended feet like Cook's, turned in with stockings. He fumbles his moustache and the sins of the world ring on his back, as Cook is always shrieking like seeing mice and calling his coalman, Mr. Kingdom, the Devil. He whips the meat-horse with ribbons on his long whip, and it pulls the coal about like heavy dead, with the devil doing everyone's fires for them with torches in his eyes and teeth. The horse dies away when he stops, with his ears saying Here beginneth. He smells full of Old

Testament at his collared edges. Cook comes out
with hard bread for him and sees mice everywhere.
The coalman is very pleased he is the Devil, and the
Devil is very clever making her think he is the
coalman. She says Lovely boy to the horse, but she
only means to the coalman, and she ought to give
him the bread, because the horse doesn't believe
her. A horse should believe when you give him
something. Her voice is all strained like muslin
through jelly, unbelieving in horses. The Devil says
little pitchers in shiny pink, and turns on his eyes.
His teeth switch out like a piano through black
orange skin. He changes back into the coalman, and
takes away the horse who makes a noise like opening bibles in his nose. He is one who shall inherit
the earth after us, it prophets all down his grey
and white mane and into the Bible of his nose, and
his tail is very meek to the coalman's boot. You go
to church and pray for the horse, who says verily
verily with his head, up the road, and has his day
of rest like everyone on Sundays. Our Father, said
very tight, hallowed be thy mane. Thy kingdom
come with yellow letters on a red cart, thy will be
done in heavy harness made of bibles. Give us this
day our daily bread from all the houses, but please
make it sugar instead. Lead us by the rein with the
tongue sagging and not into temptation which the
Devil has ready for Cook, rolled out of sight where
his arms come out of his sleeves near his waistcoat
which smells of dogs. Forgive us our trespasses up
the gravel, where Father grumbles about horsefeet.
Deliver us from evil which is eyes in bags over the
Devil's shoulder. For thine is the kingdom, and

thine rings three little bells on the horse's back, thine, thine the power and the glory like warhorses and nostrils, forever and ever, Amen all the way down the white part of a horse's head.

It isn't with suddenly, or lo, but carefully, you begin to see summer going like footsteps away, and you can see next year with long ears like a spaniel going to have puppies, and more dinners. You can examine happenings like bubbles in glass. Mysterious used to be smelling of mushrooms, and white bubbles in glass, the glass thinking a little queen into white but now it is becoming knitted into more of you. You can see when the curtains will be drawn when the night has just gone mauve. And if you try, things don't work any more in unthinking, but get bigger and work by thinking high. And dogs look up to you like people. Under tables gets silly, where it used to be mountains and tents and ships and a disaster with black beards.

One day a school has doors and windows, and play is now soldiered. Words tap with green hammers. You draw a head-horse and they say Celtic over you to each other, leaving you out, so you don't tell them Celtic is where the horse comes off the grass and onto the road and up onto the grass again. And then they pin you into uncomfort like papers together, when you want to do a different head-horse or a wall of all elephant. It is important, not important like a white pigeon puffing with coral chilblains, or a wicked Prime Minister who plots against the Kaliph, with a hat like cabbages. But as the hat can't say the whole word Imagination it can't curl up altogether into a folded full, red

cabbage. Imagination is scrubbed back into bristles
at school, flattening people. It scrubs itself in the
middle with a g. A big G opens a gate, but the child
g is a tadpole which fell out. H is a Horse's Head
over the fence, which is a quick word like a fox
disappearing. Fence has a white tail and is gone.
You can draw H out into a fence, but you must
make a horse behind it. They try and make you
see the horse in front, look, shading, but the horse
likes a standing shade under the trees in the middle
of the field. And the fence goes all round the horse,
not round you if you don't want it.

2 has a lovely arched neck for a prince's golden
bridle, and 6 has left another bit wriggling under
the spade. 5 digs into a place in front, and 8 is like
new sheets on a cold night, or sand out of the hand.
10 is a neighbour. 3 looks back and is sorry. 4 is a
clergyman. 1 is not allowed to do anything else, and
7 eats grass in the orchard. If you put them all
together, you make boredom in dust and oooos,
and you are filled with wanting sudden orchards.
It is a different boredom to wet after lunch, with
sleep coming on like long grey icy stockings over
the head and the afternoon flat and brown, stretching out like a sideways fish saying wop at the
window. It comes on in close fur lines like a jersey,
or like the boards on a pier which are two together,
letting the sea up to you in flashes like new sauce-
pans. The pier has a crown at the end, and slaps
the water back like quarrelling. It is buttoned underneath with rough shells, and underneath, waves go
like plates breaking upwards. Some of the shells
have Chinese moustaches tickling the sea, and a

man has wet boots up to his arms and a bucket full
of eels writing Eels very well. Another bucket has
poor shells with orange insides, which want the
sea back and hop like kettle lids.

Lovely day.
Yes, isn't *it. Lovely*
Too good though   We'll have to suffer for it

                         yes

                    NONSENSE
stuff and
         nonsense

It is difficult to make words look perfectly like
eels writing Eels, dog looks like frogspawn and big
DOG is completely final, even upside down. Dog
doesn't write a dog at all, but Catechism sounds
like a Scottish cat jumping over rocks. It sounds
its whiskers and prepares like John the Baptist. The
vicar comes, and you go down like posts all along
for Jesus' sake. A sinner always stands up, and is
miserable and cold in a mackintosh, and no hanky.
Hell is only dentists forever and back again unless
there's a new heaven and a new earth. But it would
still be hell with all dentists instead of people. And
Timothy will go to hell for holding himself, which

is a wickedness like Babylon and harlots which come in rows at you like tin beans.

Forever goes on and around God, who directs Forever on again if it slows down to try and make anything else. One day, if Forever runs out of doing it, God will have to mend the stretched bit in a hurry. Eternity is the stars' Forever, and is very cold and thoughtful, and Time started with God counting one, two, and becomes Eternity when he stops all of us, turning us into stars, who have anyway let Time go past them running to catch up with Forever. When Time walks slowly it is centuries. And God does care about men and ants toiling. But if God can't end Forever, and if Time gets so big that it fills everything up, it must turn and run back again into smaller than mice, and then into pins, squeezing squeezes into thinnest blackness, up into singing whiteness which is another end of blackness and Time. Time can also think so big it goes huge into music, and on down through red and blue, and into down and up, and out and out into a black balloon of enormous Time without thinking and without God, into bursting into unending black roars of Forever. O dear and O dear, each way Time faints, with thinking into black or white Eternity.

Hell is a small Forever really, and heaven is being ready for going on to New Earths, while being golden with everything, and being chosen for it if you're good by angels, who tell God about you. And sheep walk about on Judgement Day, when they have been washed white as snow by the angels, and God has a lamb up his sleeve. Goats are rude, and are sent to hell by Not Looking, and their horns toast people in the fire. If you see a goat on earth, he says Beelzebub through tight lips with his tongue out, and is one of the unspeakable, and Jesus said we should never suffer goats, but I like them. *I like* them. I *said it.* I stood up as I being a full I instead of a small you, and said it. So there, God. I'll say it again. *And again. I Like Goats*, and you can send a thunderbolt for a lie. I am a brazen image, so ugh and a dose of worms and a plateful of diarrhoea. Ha, ha. God. I shall sit on an altar and pee. Now I know you can't get at my secrets. In the snail's shell of me entirely, going round and round and whee, *me*. And you are *you*. And them are *them*. And good dogs, *down there. Sit!* And damn you. I said, *Damn you.* Universe and Damn. You can sit with a stuffy nose in the Bible, saying Forever in gold and Doom in black, and pinning secrets sharply out of peoples' shells. Because I am getting all the I together into *Me*, I am making butter all round me of *Me*. And I can even see winter if I stretch thinking.

Call this a stick and you assert.
Call it not a stick and you negate.
Now, do not assert nor negate, and what would
    you call it?
Speak   Speak
I broke the stick in two, asking 'what is this?'

Well! Well is a little road which can lead into doing or not doing, or questions, or long waiting for asking why you haven't. And I'm beginning to say *Well*, and waiting to see if I shall. It is like a sheep that nibbles and look up tasting a smile, and nibbles and walks, and runs and stops, looking into a long way off, with fright at the end with its ears up.

I don't like watching people, because they look up and see, and then you have to start off talking like pushing small oclocks backwards, which is tiring.

Talking can be like feeling shining furniture, or easily fingered over like a brass tray, or very clever and winding like two candlesticks made of talk going in and out and up and down and no talking suddenly where they get heavy. Or talking is very full and excellent, going slowly round like carpets by fires, making countries, with people climbing steps up to bannisters of laughing coming down again. Talking can be carriage horses with How do you do heads, and come here at once, said like a black monkey's hand with yellow eyes and shutting down his eyebrows. And ladies, who may have husbands, who beak speaking bits out of the por-ridge-talk, like crows with blue eyes watching the bird table. Husbands talk like sideboards with bottles and blue plates, and a bronze horse not really trying to break away. They may be fathers too, and speak smearing embarrassments like spilling lemonade at parties or when a puppy has been and you can't smack it with visitors. This is — and they push their children like taking shopping out when you get home. Diana, Cynthia, Pam, Jennifer, Timothy. They are false, smiling like uncomfortable dogs. Fathers should say *This* and *This*, meaning it. *My daughter*.

Sometimes talking goes just right, like making yourself a real china dog with spots and a round tail, with moving colours of pink and copper and a secret tied on his collar. On one side he goes into a moving copper-green and on the other bronze-pink, which as you move him turn all over each other like some fish. He has good gracious eyes like watching faces in stories. Talking like this is full-up, like real cream, and like cows lying down on satisfied butter.

And some talking goes on after bed like small walruses in corners, and some is awful, like Bluebeard forbidding in cupboards, and going over what you've done in a downstairs voice. It is like opening a door and there you are, holding yourself. They could small you over with countenances when you were just you, like a creased white puppy, but now the I is very quick with unthinking and jumps with it nicely, I just came down for a drink. And a thinking Please. A very quick head hop like that poem's jackdaw, hiding a ring.

Disasters don't happen so much now, because you have antlers out being careful to the wind all round. The I takes hold of the you part, and you take things, singing like open canaries. It is a lovely feeling like hurrying a whole family of badgers into bed.

Sometimes that leopard nearly sees you, and you leave a gasp standing there when the I jumps out and catches on a branch out of reach, and the you is left stuck and seeing concrete. You must get the I down quickly for saying whatever puts the leopard back. The you part sits all fur like a bad dog, until the I can get everything smooth again, like ordered cucumber sandwiches.

One day there was a whole £1 note for the laundry and the I choked the you like dragging hard, sitting dogs about by the collar. The wind's hand was stirring porridges of loose air around corners, and your breath. Pussy, Pussy, Puss. You had to go behind the beech hedge smelling of dry sponges, and sit and make a great soft loaf of Looking. And like eating the whole world's strawberries only begotten with the biggest Love. And you went past two policemen like being bread and butter very close right through, and you ran like fast, red tigers to Mrs. Browning for six baby rabbits and well I never like Cook's cuckoo clock at six o'clock. And went back through the boggy bit with the four waiting unseen rhinoceroses, and a horrid fur dog on your chest. And pulled in coming-home like heavy ropes.

> *A pound! A whole pound!*
> *But I know I left it*
> *on the table here*
> > *look*
> > > *just here*
> > *Gee do you think Deffy could have*
> *Bad blood there   I don't*
> *care*

93

        what   *Ormonde says*
                         bad blood   *I was*
reading somewhere that they steal for
              affection !   *But we* adore   *her   I'm*
always telling her   telling her   oh there's the bell

The rabbits were white with Chinese full-stops
all over, and all the you looked at them like Christ
so loved the world, and the I joined in and said
Mine. My rabbits, and the you didn't have to agree
for once, it was being all full of rabbits with white
feet, and one sitting up and saying something in
black Chinese, very fast. Their ears were filled up
to the top with black, and everything was joyful
and triumphant like God seeing the good and resting.
    And then Mr. Loving finding holes for lettuces
and Whatever being said in long blue letters going
up like chimneys. And No and multiply and I was
given them and *No*. All over like a moose, and
Father hanging in Bluebeard's cupboard. And wanting to crack heads and hard boiled eggs and *why*.
And *No* like dropping the well cover, and the nerve
and no-where to keep them, and *No*. And not even
one, but SIX said like the beginnings of a disaster
like Funeral Parlour. And *No*, I'm adamant, like
King Solomon in a stone urn. And I hate you and
I hate you. I hope God spits you out and revenges
on you. *I hope you fall down the lavatory forever.*
And the white rabbits with Chinese all over them
have gone into a toothache of tears, and the end
of the short world is cut off for the you and I gone
into a sad bear of sleep.

Now I can see the days wired like peanuts, and a net full of months hung up, and right at the very end there is a year on the telephone.

Monday can be a white dog with a bad paw, taking his time, and Tuesday is blue and says that's better, giving the week's ball a push, and Wednesday is an orange daisy. Thursday is nearly blue and very tall, looking over for Sunday who is still asleep, and dark red smiling Friday sits very close to Saturday, and Saturday feels like a small Christmas in bright red. Sunday is a long clean sheet and smells of horseradish and has paper feet for afternoons.

You can fit the days into squares and walk them definitely, but they are all different and never the same ones come round again, except dreary dinners and the yawning bread van. Sometimes an already worked-out dread happens though, which hangs over us like a crystal coincidence in the wind. It can be ordained by God pointing, but nearly always happens without God, and is very old like Greek thunderstorms. And sometimes a slow grazing comes on, and you know the next word you say will have been hung up like a silver ball in the world's next room for you to say again, and you say it, re-knowing it, as it goes slowly like fatal mice through you. Not only words, but roads and doors into knowing-behind, where you've been and happened there without it saying, until now. You stop and fit the feeling on like gloves, and I've been here before, like saying it backwards coming out of a cave, and the world takes a breath, listening. And then it all canters on again and the Greek feeling goes away, not looking at you.

Well, one day all the squares you can fit Tuesday and Wednesday in, end in a black one, and that's Fate sitting on a long board of squares nearly at Forever, which is the end of you.

And it's all set out for someone else.

Sometimes you wonder if someone else has said your word before, and you are the next to ring it, or if another you will come along after, hearing a long hello from outside everything back past dying Greece.

But now words are being soled and heeled down, and you can see them like chops on the counter, definite chops, without excursions. They are put down like change, saying what they are, and you cannot make them into other things. And they speak in black now and not in colour, and they cannot smell themselves. And sums make railways out of sixpences, with half-crowns beginning to get rich, and roan ten shillings. And five pounds is very reverent with swans' writing.

Learning Music is getting it up out of lines, like drying tadpoles, and middle C is caught up on the fence getting through. It is doing sums with o which come out music instead, and jumps with a tail like black lambs. It makes hard and cold listening, not like full music which makes battles and the sea turns rainbows over and attacks God. It is different to noise, and birds doing it in a different silver.

Some music pulls you all out into green strings of wanting to be water, or right outside being men. And you can't believe the sky with music, and it tells you your end in uttermost hearing. The vicar's

music is different, some is like long well-trained
dogs and he goes over it with a proper voice, and
hymns are all fenced in and end in gates of Amen.
But some, which is like God playing into your head,
fills you up with steps made of amethysts and the
future, and doesn't have to be only in church. The
man who specially used it, always takes a deep
breath, and stops and rolls it up at the end with his
own Amen, so that you know it's his always. And
you feel all put together again like an angel. It is
very difficult to come out into the day again afterwards with seeing gold and whole bits of God, and
then other people's talk as sharp and annoying as
lavatory paper. How you can get all that music out
of the world, taking pieces of sea and jewels and
some birds, and making countries, and pushing
death over, and God turning to look with emeralds,
how you can get all that music out of your ears
and into forever is a too difficult sum for ordinary
people, and the piano won't go for you at all. You
can say I to middle C, and you to E flat, which is
a headache coming on, but that's all that happens.
And yet music is all strung up like Tuesday to
Wednesday really, and pennies leading up finally
into the bit of Forever where people get too tired
to count, although it still goes on without them.
Because men can't go *right* on like God can. And
primroses come up, and everything goes round the
world in summer and winter too, which leads into
centuries and then Time again.

It is funny how you always end up with Time,
and then Forever. They seem to beckon, and men
want to get to them one day, counting. Tuesday and

97

Wednesday walking men into Forever, and you in it just for when it says Now. The present is now, and it will last you all the time you're alive, and then you hand it to God when you go up, and it's the past. People give presents for birthdays, which come too. Like Tuesday and Wednesday. The future is like a house with a smoking chimney round a bend and you don't know it, a very Greek feeling which wants deeply to *know* like looking into ponds with your eyes taken out.

The future is Time coming at you, but only for men, who count it coming, as really it's going away into Forever, and people are catching it up when they die.

Do you know I've thought very hard at exactly midnight, and I think really hard, that one day, which isn't really a day as it will have passed everything, the whole black Forever will grow and grow so that it's filled up with Eternity, and men will have gone into thoughts all the way up, and God is the head Thought. And everything will be one huge, full-up Thought, thinking itself out and back again, round and back, bright and thinking exploded Wisdom all over. It's like having a head gone bang completely with Wisdom over a very long time, and God at the end of Forever, who has thought it all out and back again into the one big, whole, marvellous Thought, and going past himself into God and God and nothing and nothing. But you cannot go on thinking too hard, otherwise the stars knock you down with thinking, and stride you back dizzy into the day.

So much is going on, not just guinea-pigs in

hutches and birds flying, and money out for the butcher and a horse on three legs scratching his nose, and people all over the place, and us, but these great big Thinkings thinking us all. And no one seems to *see*, even though they try a bit in church.

It makes you want to cry, and then say Hurray to a snail.

Deffy likes Bach
Well yes she says so

      Oh you mean the Schumann
                          very well

Go away for now Deffy   Daddy's
           Playing

Keep that child
        out   *May*

Now go and play dear
        that's a good girl

    Must ring Brabham on Monday
       what an awful thing he's blind Gee
    Good piano tuners often are
            did you know
  Brabham's excellent, probably better
           being blind
                  give him tea

Surprises happen best when it's not birthdays and undone surprises which you can guess, but a stone with something a long time before in it, and a six-pence there among stones which knocks on your eyes like a bit of an unlucky wizard's feelings still left there on the stones, or that sideways one which takes a bang out of *you being you* when you find five wild brown and green eggs in a bird's plaited nest on the ground, or thinking deer behind a tree and *there is one*. Built of real deer and not just your smoked thought wanting. There's a smaller knock finding brown hen-house eggs, but this is a domestic surprise to you walking along and then bang, right in the middle of you being you, knocking your whole mould sideways. It's funny how summer comes very clear suddenly on a winter day, coming along on the wind. In summer people say a *lovely day*, yet they aren't you, filled up with summer and hedgehogged into being you with happiness. You wish you could walk backwards for a whole day, looking up at the sky, and people a long way off behind rocks, talking, when the sun has pinned you and a starfish into a small, thoughtful half-forever with sandy knees.

It is funny how there is an old you which is really a forgotten animal, and most people have sat down hard and squashed the fur. It sniffs nice days, and hasn't got to think money, and likes to lie down and give into the sun pushing down the grass. It looks up through rainbow eyelashes and is deeply sorry men spoiled it. It goes under the moon, listening on strings, and is older than Greece, going back near the starfish in a pool.

Animals know it, not having to Look Out, there are People, but saying Animal through their noses. Without saying you're a horse and so am I, or a cat which slides it out like best friends, not meaning, or a dog. And you don't have to stand up saying it back, or worse still I'm a human, which they never want to know unless they're parrots. It's being warm all over and fur through the heart, and thinking with whiskers, and eyes closed in the sun, and very delicate smellings like fairy stories told by wind. And not being hurt because there's no need to be hurt if you say to a lion just lion, thinking of the sun with his paws in the air and one white whisker among the others.

And it's not rude if you're an animal.

I wish I was a hedgehog being happy in little dots, or birds flying, having sky journeys and trees for feet, and not a human having to stand up all the time and worry about all that forever at the end of all the world's sums, and being good and being married and drying up into bones. And even then perhaps having to go on *thinking into everyone else's Forever.* But not a great monkey, I would hate to sit like a great monkey looking out at Forever, and not being able to work it out because God stopped them. It worries them, with thinking and then unthinking coming on, and they're very sad. People shouldn't laugh at them because they have failed being absolute men. It must be sad being on the wrong side of God, who thought a big ugh into gorillas, but let men through to help him think out Forever finally.

And then my animal goes away under its sad,

warm, forgetting eyelashes, and you are left with a sweet smell in the wind's grass which makes you think of all your yesterdays.

How shall I escape from the wheel of Life and Death?
Who puts you under restraint?

I like the feeling of the something-else world, which goes into all your corners. It is part of the knocking at your head, and the untold surprises.

It is something that came there, and then went away from around it, leaving it behind. Like a gold ring among sea pebbles, and like all the brown and green and turquoise eggs. It is left shining in a small emptiness not belonging and feeling very Greek, standing like left toys all night in the garden.

And there is another part of the world which grown-ups say Yes dear and they don't see for waiting. They walk on and on again, and make you rough inside worrying that they don't see.

All your seeing was peeled back when they hung up the caught fox. He was shot by Tom, slapped down onto the path of his running, and people won't look with real *see*.

It's not because he's just stiff and uninterested dead, but because he's got bits of his night still there, all his things of him being him while people are only bumps in beds while he runs over the lawns, smelling of curried earth.

His eyes are still full of his ginger run, his face made for going, and his black nose making thumb prints on the wind bringing him his news. His paws took him past mushrooms, and the end of the moon went along on his tail.

Poor, poor fox, to be made an examining for flies, and not being a creature again.

Why won't people look properly for him, like they use with funerals. Not flowers, because he is a fox, but feeling a very kind Amen to him.

Yes, ha ha.   Growing every day.
Say hello to Mr. Rideout
Say hello
She's shy   Hello Deffy, you know me
I'm Rosemary's Daddy.
    Now, do you know what I do *here?*
That's right! *I'm a* bank manager!
My word, you are *clever . . .*

Everyone ought to feel their petals opening for everything, because it is only this that rivers into the true Forever. It makes you so rough inside wanting so badly for people to *see*. Even God can't include him too much, writing another FOX and that's all, as there are so many men going all the time, and little boxes needed for sparrows.

Oh dear, oh dear God. Look down on this merciful fox for us, and let St. Peter have him up, like someone had that lame lion, and someone else had a friendly wolf for his very own. Not just that, but *Care*, not just ticking him off.

If I died now, just died, I'd have to be all straight in a mothball nightie, with those lilies honking with nothing coming out, and I think they'd have a folded angel put up.

I'd rather have a Greek horse full of trumpets and Who's There, but that was only done when there wasn't a church with white clergymen, and people were buried in better places like mountains and seashores, being nymphs and warriors and with lovely words like orchids going round, and bulls with flowers on, and no Let us pray like iron railings. And do you know, I don't think it is just God ticking us all off and saying you and you, and hell marked in red like lit-up Gentlemen. And all those angels on a glassy sea. If they landed they'd skid into the throne, which is why they've got better wings than clumsy ducks on the ice.

I don't think God waits with a bun, or there's a lift going down for sinners, and I don't even think he's a He. Or a She. But a huge It all round, going into and out of the fox and me, and making the fox a past and me a new, and everything going by like a black river knowing it all.

Not just someone like a much bigger Abraham, but Everything and Nothing fitting together in a perfect sum of A+.

*In the three Worlds, Everything depends on
     the mind.
If the mind is not at rest, what are palaces and
     mansions?
Horses and cattle, the Seven Treasures —
Of what avail are they?*

And people don't see how full of flower a flower is, standing being a flower, with flowers saying here and a leaf saying there and there and one nearly there, and keeping some green back for a tomorrow.

People spoil it with saying *We* all the time, and standing in skirts and going ugh back at ties.

I want to be a real I, without Yes Dear and a Fancy, coming out like a pink squiggle on the cake. And Hurry Up like pulled dogs' leads, and awfulness like a squashed toad where the good runs out. Why can't there be a space between awfulness and the good where you just *are*, not doing it. Like animals. Getting grown up means not so much awfulness, and putting a foot either side on to the good edges. Unless there's a huge one at the end, like murder or marrying someone else several times, or having a baby in the kitchen.

The highest thinking is thinking a deep Buddha under a cherry tree, with so much pink going on it turns into prayers, which don't come out as Our Father, but which go up like you smoking blue all over. Anyone can do it, I don't know why they have to be specially monks to dwell on Forever subjects.

No, not today. No thanks. Come, Deffy.

No, I don't think I know you, Mrs. Er — I think you must have the wrong house. Yes, er, she is very dark, m'mm very much like your Dosha. Hello Deffy. Dosha — what a pretty name. Deffy   Is she? No, she's our own. Dear little Daughter. I don't know any Smiths I'm afraid. No. O here — Dosha — here's sixpence, dear. Yes, haha, they could er be sisters. Good luck?   oh   Thank you!   thank you.

Gee what was I to say? She even asked me. Said she was the image of one of her brother's children. I think we've done something very, very unwise. Ormonde and his 'gypsy orphan'   We've got to talk to him, G. She's either got to know — of course, much later, or we've simply got to make sure she's never told. But will Ormonde tell her, then? One day? That wretched man. Gee, we must have been insane to think it would work

Of course we Love her. But
I'm a nervous wreck over it all —

and now that
wretched Circus

O. I could write O a hundred times with clouds, the Circus is coming on the Common. It is like Father Christmas with feeling, but harder with dark men. I will polish my good so that I'm like a cat with stroked manners.

They said Elephants like fircones dropping off

the people all the way up the road, the Elephants,
Look, the Elephants.

One is coming with a John the Baptist kind of
coming, pushing the air back against the houses,
and with a red carpet on his head. He is pondering
up and up, and now he is treading all over your
heart. He has tramps' feet for skin, and it thunders
dry skin all over him, oozing him into bulges and
swings. His feet go down like someone large on a
piano stool, and he is looking at me with judgement
written in white in his eye. He is an Our Father all
over with Elephant. And his ears are saying Aloof,
Aloof. His trunk comes over with Allow Me, but
he gets slapped by his rajah and sucks the sting
in a mouth like knickers. And there's Another and
Another, with sighs and knitted tails and huge
rudenesses hidden behind. With so much Prepare
the way on their fronts, it is funny how their tails
say such a quiet blanket of a small Amen when
they go.

Then there's a distance like space breathing before
making another coming, and there's a white llama,
springy like ladies being young behind, but half a
bishop in front walking in careful slippers. O, and
it has a feather-duster baby, pinking like someone
tweaking a mat on a washing line, God has painted
a black O twice on the mother, and a brown D
around the baby's tail, which dongs its trot like a
church bell-rope.

Oh and look, look at the up and down zebra
which butts into following, his man digging in his
feet like running spades to keep him back in his
crossed red bridle. He takes all your looking into

him and over all his maps like a music animal ruled around, swinging bells of black railways all round him and writing his tail with a paint brush. His mane dusts him all over into his wriggles, and his polished prune eye slices you into a quick half. He has little saucepan feet rattling with his all-over boiling, wasping his knees, pushing at his wanting. He has gathered all his black threads into his face with thumb lines, his forehead puzzling Arabic into saying Dizzy. He's pushed his space so hard that the road has to wait for the next ones, and they are four camels, stepping over silent doorsteps, with their hair holding bags up all over them, and their faces telling them I believe in the Holy Camel. They are posted to each other along ropes, and stroke back soft looking at you with girls' eyes in yellow mirrors. They go by like IxIxIxI, multiplying their four exactly.

Then a lot of dressed-up people being cowboys, and ladies skipping on white legs which wobble further up, walking flat with pink wound-up shoes. They have young hair with ribbons and dancing frills, but old necks and shoulders like geese hung up for Christmas. When they smile, like someone wiping a mirror, their necks rope up and down like string hammocks. Some of them are really young, and very pretty, all fitted into their jelly well because they're young. And the men crack whips and look Indians made with poster paints, and cowboys, but really only with lorry drivers' shirts, and clowns which don't really work in daylight and you hope they don't touch you. Ever. There is a kind of awfulness, like peoples' bones buried and white sitting somewhere near them, and their faces put up a white hand, not letting you in, with laughing that doesn't mean fun. There's a black man who is nice and really means it, like chocolate blackmange, with hard wobbles and ladders up his stomach where his chest curtains part, and he has a leopard's coat round his behind.

Oh and the horses coming, hello horses, oh wait for my eyes to net you all and make a draught of horses like those fishes. Each horse saying I am, some holding black back and shining it into coming out again, and some golden ones with altar-cloth manes and raffia tails, and some white with pink surprised on their noses and with allsorts eyes, all their tails waving flags and all their manes Coronations, and some varnished brown with echoes all through them, and others woven into marmalade, and two big cart-horses with policemens' lips and tails stuck into their fat behinds like taps into barrels. One is a banana cream and has blue eyes like fair people, and the other is a raspberry fool with black edges all round. Their shoes show quickly like someone flicking water off their hands, and their people walk near them in cloaks like the Devil on his best behaviour.

Oh these are the best, these are the best of all, oh look at these, look. Look. Fishes are jumping on them, and they're throwing black tar into your eyes, and you could paint them just like that, here and here and a great splat just there.

They are coal dropped on a snowy path, and ink going into interested water, and newts colliding with fishes, and starlings fizzing up over an opened lemonade hedge, and God getting a new paint box out in a hurry.

Look at the spotted horses, in white lordships' coats and with peppermint eyes, all splottered and plopped and studded and jetted and sprinkled and exploded all over with black. Each one is a Horse written out in a spotted language, with full stops and exclaims all over them in Persian and Arabic, and with a Chinese poem around their tails. If you could put all their black music together you could play a whole horse going Pom Pom, and call him Sonata, which is graceful like his neck. And all their red harness is doing them up like a Christmas.

But they go by like the sea going away from the stones, and leaving only the stones tinkling on your ears and eyes.

There are lions coming, King lions with their furs up, and Queen lions which are flatter than their husbands, framed like pictures on wheels. The Kings stretch their looks back to Africa, leaving everyone out, and the Queen lions rug themselves into sleep or flypaper their tongues up.

The next picture rolls the tigers along, and they have white pin-cushions on their cheeks and dangerous Chinese written on their faces. Their orange has been hit with black twigs, and on their tails it goes round and round like gramophones and ends in a small gong. They can see the ghosts that we can't in broad daylight behind us, and you could post a black letter down their mouths. One yawns a slow, pink Porridge, and smiles ice. He has pink pillows under his feet. Leopards are smaller danger, and they have rain which has fallen off stones over them, and leaves blowing against them which have pressed on their coats, and falling off, made them leopards in the wind. They are very careful not to be caught by the ghosts, and the cheetah by himself has long black crying and coins pressed all over his sand.

And there's a bear drawing a line up and down blindness, and some wolves feeling a corner coming up in their middle, trying to find their grey time ticking up and down the cage.

And a white woman with pigeons waving a white goodbye all the time with them on her arms as she walks.

And there's a little man who has bulges and has been cut off like a sausage, but his head carries him along and he has spread newt's hands and walks scuffling a ball along which isn't really there, with his legs. He pulls along a little black-winkle dog on a liner's hope.

And then the emptiness comes along behind, putting the road back and the houses down again, and stringing buses back. And the drums and all the music goes after itself away up the road, and then a little bit of red trumpet comes back, and a thump like two doors, and then your ears come back like dogs being called, and your eyes get pushed aside by buses.

They are blowing the huge peppermint tent up with people, and the wind is fingering wiggles into the galleon flags on the top like pleating paper. It looks up again and again over the hedge as though Mr. Browning has pulled down the biggest sunblind in all the world over all the cowpats. And the cows stare at the dangerous grass which smells of stripes and squashed elephant. And the sun has bitten somebody through the yellow bars.

> *I kept hanging the moon*
> *On the pine tree and taking it off,*
> *Gazing at it the while.*

It is there, it is there behind my diamond, but I cannot fill my days into pillows of soft love for Mother and Father. I can see Father planned out all down the gravel without one weed, with the salmon newspaper which flops on the carpet like posting fish, and smelling of clean new dogs. Father's shoes suck very prosperous embarrassments on the black and white floors of banks, where there are altars for money, and the people pray on both sides with giving and receiving. They hush like dentists before pain, and are dearly beloved we are gathered together with their fingers sponging the money and finding no snails in its lettuce. They centipede over it saying in frog hops, two-four-six-eight, and write very fast a pushed *viddy viddy squot*. And Father writes Hawhawaton and a swan's neck, and makes a careful shadow on the blotter with it.

The Bank's own horse has broken his elastic and is not looking at tripping over, with his back feet on his piece of promenade rock. All the money and the people doing it sit in cages behind the suspicions, exchanging altars. I wish it was lions in the security, and clouded leopards in the silver, and a five pound zebra with gilt stripes smelling of church like a unicorn does.

And the door would have Manager. Do not feed. And he'd be a whale behind it all, in a big glass tank, balancing sixpences on his fountain. It would be interesting to see a whale, but it isn't with only whole Managers with lavatory paper collars, being very clean with money.

Father goes over the lawn, which must worry the worms underneath, and rings people up for Bristol Cream and Armadillos, standing a bit backwards and making it all right like the vicar.

Once Father and Mother went out, beautifully chromiumed in the car, and the day began to grow over with furry brass with the sun beginning to think of thunder, and it changed the brass into mauve a long way behind Mr. Browning, thinking it up tremendously. All the birds felt a terrific Greek foretell coming, and the last sun switched all the trees on, until they felt faint with the mauve standing over them now, and one growl coming. The leaves began pointing look out and the flowers brought out all their pink and red and electric yellow and held them up. A blink comes out of the mauve, and a longer lion follows, a paw coming up to the edge of the kitchen garden. But he pulls it back and has to think himself up again. Now there's a much bigger jump and a split and the lion reaches nearly here. Mr. Browning's farm and the field has gone under upright seas of rain spears, which are hissing as they come. The clouds are slithering now

113

and the mauve draws in the world for a breath, and I've got the front door shut and mustn't touch metal.

The Lion of Judah opens the sea up and it roars onto the door, and he falls on the house with his teeth splitting it with lightning, standing all over the garden. And then there's a long dark silence, but he hasn't gone, he's still standing with his feet in the corners of the garden, waiting for my heart to roll out of the house like a marble.

He has sent a red ball to find me out. It rolls on itself and shudders with fire, turning over and over very slowly and searching along over the lawn. And suddenly rising over the beech trees and running down over the pond, breathing in and out for me. *Where are you. Where are you. I can see.* I look into the Chinese screen; make room for me, silk herons and storks. If I can stitch myself in with you, it cannot find me. I can see it through the window, and it sees me, and turns rolling silently back. There's a terrible red pulled-in bang, and the windows fly off like minnows, and then they come back and say did you see the Fireball, the Fireball. A natural phenomenon, which is said with little black hole eyes looking down at a spread-out phenomenon, which is like an eiderdown of examining amazement when the moon is ringed like a blue onions. Lions say a tall quiet PHENOMENON too, when they lift their whiskers up roundly, peeling a yawn away.

Father turns his head away and smiles like a monkey-puzzle with meaning. Good night is said like the last bit of sun.

Other fathers are men with daughters saying Daddy, *Daddy*, and they have yellow hair, but I am dark and haven't their blood in my lines. And afternoons picnic with them, tying the little girls' ribbons with big hands and hairs going under their watch straps like a loose bear, and their Mummy with summer shoes and yellow cakes with a cherry.

He's another bad
influence, too
He's drunk half the time —
It isn't right, *Gee, and that huge stallion — it's*
not right. Of course she sees. And I don't like the
way she hangs round him all the time. And one day
she'll get bitten and then you'll have *to do some-*
thing.

something

I love you, I love you, all done up in a parcel of me for you. But not for the pink satin-edged blankets Mother hangs up on her loving. I don't want after my bath to be dried by her, I will do myself roughly without. She kneels there and I feel she is very stupid to cry. The diamond that is me is only for my burning, I cannot give it away or I will fall in.

I think of my lost Father in the leaves, he is winter, and is blown away under the trees and sits under the glowing trunks with the snow, sadly for a little while. He cannot decide, and the sun changes his mind for the green to come through, and father walks away for his second coming, against a pink sky dying with frost.

Mother oh mother, lay my head on the sweet primroses, promising me the sky, and bees comforting the orchard. You turn away under the secret red toadstools, and where the moss makes a sorrow for me, and you lay the afternoon for me to wear like a dress of fine-spun rain to be born in. Somewhere you put me together, but my own diamond is to guard me from falling apart. Except for animals, who can come in at any time and polish it.

No one really needs my diamond yet except animals, although Mother and Father want to cut it out and make strawberries and cream of soft love. Love is a diamond, not little love like pink and lemon and white-ringed cakes, or the long white drooping love in sandals which is a Jesus blancmange or Brigadier and Lady Gerald and all the suitable daughters watching for it through binoculars. But one side is nests, and the other is a dark man for you, and the other is holding out your hand to Buddha.

The dark man will have a diamond too, and you can polish them together, sitting on the grass.

A Lion-father looks lions into you, and another father is the big black horse which comes to Mr. Browning's and walks around owning Paddy on a long white rein. He looks round at me in the stable, where they are very respectful with voices in slippers, and won't let me in, like an Emperor. He has silver chains on his doorposts, and he says a very soft Daughter of Jerusalem through his velvet.

One day I went in and Paddy never saw, and the father-horse put all his watching on me like a magnifying glass on brown, and I reached up and put my diamond on his neck. And I said Oh second father, and he made rubber shrubberies with his lips all over my face like a mouse in a polishing cloth.

They locked his door afterwards, and I could only hear his black rattling inside, like angry coal, because he had once killed someone by the throat. He would never have killed me though, because he gave me his own brown diamond too, but Paddy shoved my words down like pressing a spaniel.

Paddy is nice, with a waistcoat smelling of moss sandwiches and white hair down like a goose's head. Horses listen carefully to his water talk, and he has special hands for them. Father's hands are like new kittens, and couldn't comfort the oil over horses. Paddy satins out Sir Robert's tail, and mothers his mane and face-fringe with a sponge, and nourishes his black mould all over. I can talk properly with Paddy, and he doesn't strain at you being children. He says things that matter, which get stuck afterwards inside your ears like wise goose-grass. He says sure a lot, like long seashells. He'll not harm me, his Uncle Paddy. Sure he's nothing to be jealous about, at all. He bounces at all on his talk's wall at the end, and sometimes twice. And doesn't the Good Lord see to it that the childer come to no harm. He says. And sure, he knows I've not the interest in the ladies now, God bless him, though I've still the eye for a decent filly to pick for himself there. Paddy blesses God onto people a lot, even when he goes to sleep suddenly with all his brown bottles soldiered along the floor. He goes around the summer with Sir Robert, and people pay them for walking round giving them foals. And Sir Robert makes a black coronation of falking at the end of his white rein, on the edges on summer's ring, gulping other horses into his eyes and knitting thunder inside.

And I wish I could marry Sir Robert, turned into a prince.

Mother says that man's an influence, like rinsing out a bad taste, and goes to the fishmonger.

O look Deffy *— what* are *they, Mr. Macmillan? Tench? Oh I've never seen tench before, and* that's *a carp. Oh yes, the monks used to eat them, didn't they. On Fridays . . .*
Ugh — fish make me . . . squirm, Mr. Macmillan — I prefer them dead. yes. O and a pound of smoked haddock too please   It never looks *like fish —*
  Deffy   come on   she's always so
       fascinated   its   unnatural

It is worrying at the fishmonger, where fishes bleed into his baths, and groan with silence in stopped shouts. Big brills and turbots are useless like come down kites. They must have skidded backwards and forwards through their green sky

118

on their long string up to the fisherman, and the mackerels' quiver has ended in a gasp upwards like a bent arrow with a bloody point. Sprats are the five thousand fishes left over, sufficient unto the day, rained into bags for people to take away, and congers still dare everyone. Soles O dear O dear and look twice, and some big ones have tried to get ugh past a bubble. Only the salmon's growl of blood is caught up and held back on his beckoning teeth, his anger's varnish has hardened over his cockerel's eye. Skates say Desolation hung up, and clap one hand on their marble. Their smile is pinned out like a letter-box on them, like a clown's, in spite of their white underneath calamity. It is all coming and going in silver and pink and orange spots, and frenzies and slides into a stopped choke, with the sea waving on the sands at the funeral of all the ended fishes. And they bleed and bleed their seaweed blood into the green china fountain in the middle of the fishmonger's shop, and he tips bits of umbrella fins and astonished heads into parcels for cats.

He has big fishes in the fountain which are his pets, and they plane and gape like open handbags, and they sigh with gold as they turn over. The fishmonger catches one and holds it up, saying Lord and Forsaken in dark green, with its own coins stitched down its wet leather. It is like a money fish with Chinese feelings all over, and it lies with just one fin making a sad old man's hello. Put him back, oh put him back, he has stopped going on, and is crying back in his patience to where the struggling is. In the fountain he goes around a dark green 8 of refreshes, with his Time going on again with water. Where it sprinkles from the fountain, on the top of his waters' table, he comes up and waterlilies a gulp of You, said like a polite green jug. Sometimes they will all do it, waving their tails' chiffon and making small p's between the You.

It is very strange, and needs thinking about without all these people, how the fishes live with you living too, you in a hard upstairs with nice grass and only rain coming down, and them going up and down through all their mirrors, with no banging because it's water curtseying in brown to them. It is more than even birds breathing, but fishes are surrounded by immense wanderings of oiled mystery which can't be done up easily into a tidy flat knowing.

One day the fishmonger has a porpoise and a sturgeon both together in his window, and was very pleased. They were so big they gave out stand back like an accident with buses. The poor porpoise looked as though he had had his treat spoiled, his smile was left behind like someone keeping it up still with fingers. He had little eyes screwed into his fat, and he sat with his tail gone down like a leather anchor, and his flippers shawled against his sides. The sturgeon still sniffed at a long dismay coming along at him, and his long pirate's trunk had belts of rivets. He looked as though if you undid his screws you could unwind his strips for a church door. He had a feeling of bishops on his nose for smelling out wrongdoers, but his eyes had nothing coming in or going out, it was a little stone of never seeing or wanting seeing, because it wasn't there all the time he took nosing down past all those dinosaurs, and leaving the old worlds behind for coal. His mind never came too, like ours did, chattering in bushes and then rushing out with us when we were real men at last. Something in him cannot get past all those curled up stone worlds and the old crawled seas and the dinosaurs going blind to their days.

I can't bear to see all the poor fishes with yesterday painted in grey on them with mouthfuls of Gomorrah in their clamped wilderness, laid out with us inspecting like all the sins of the world, slapped wet sins waiting for God's marble hand to slide their red open into the devil's waiting buckets. And the soles to heaven for St. Peter's golden breadcrumbs, while he walks about in his dressing gown and his keys, and his fingers tucked into two turbots.

The fishmonger had a shark once, still ready like a gun loaded by cold bitten-off hands. It was barrelled for coming on, with dreads oiling up into shapes through black water, and a fin for slitting thoughts like terrible opened golf balls. It had dreamed my nights before I was me, the sea dreaming me in pale green, with the shark turning, turning, blind with a long cold looking, nosing among my filaments of water, tuning me into his vision with his electric eye switching him on and off as he touches my red current. I see him whining above me, where the sun sprinkles us with the sea's falling alphabet of lights, and I am lizarded with scales of horror. And sometimes I'm standing on the white sand, safe, so safe, and there is a small blue strip of happy water near my castle. But it changes, promising a black coming which wires the water back by *thinking me*, and I cannot think back.

He is always there, changing the yellow sands to sawed bones, and sighting down a line of red ocean to drill my mind. He is in my world and in my mind's world, and I have seen him move blackly under the agitated red water-lilies, his fin a vanished time on a black sundial. He is under the white ones now, which are sparkling and writhing with the hump of his rising. You mustn't look then. You must never look. To see him would dream your world back before God had begun on the black, as first he had to think it.

Run from the uneasy, lipping water-lilies, before he rises to watch you run, leaving his terrible streaming head on the marble centuries of the silent pond, sunk like a dead white fish behind the high yew hedges like a funeral for all water.

The statues, ghosted back into slots in the blinkered hedge, see nothing. There are ladies, with perfect ideas on the left of their sugared eyes, and the knotted man wound up in snakes and a full dentist's *argh!* a fat baby shooting at nothing, and a bent Mercury feeling Monday terribly in undone sandals.

The sound of someone
Blowing his nose with his hand;
The scent of the plum flowers !

er
They're creatures from mythology, dear. Old
tales. Of course there weren't really those things,
they were — made up. People's ideas of — what —
Like ghosts

     Like ghosts

          dear ghosts

One day the king of the oaks dropped my father's acorn, and he's waiting for me to find him. He stands under the oak trees waiting, with the hundreds of years blowing in his hair. The leaves come down on his shoulders, and sometimes he puts his arms out and the snow goes slowly whispering over his face, and quietens him into white all through the night.

Father, dear father, I hear you in the night, and I undo my soul for you to find me easily. I tell all the oak trees, but they go on up through their years with their sky's winter netted and journeyed with sorrows, and in summer pulling their leaves over their heads like jerseys crocheted with shade.

And father stands in their shadow where the grass smells of longing, and he clips the red and white candles on the chestnut trees for Spring's Christmas.

Mother doesn't go away. Ever. She talks in the woods and puts my cheek onto moss, and laughs sometimes through birds, and brings out primroses to where the sun can sit for a while. She thinks out the violets, and hears for me a cuckoo while I look at ferns, and her eyes are silver with waterfalls in a place I've never been to. Sometimes the moon watches me for her, while she rests with her hands full of sleeping brown mice, who love her.

One day my mother left the sea, saying goodbye sadly to the pink shells, and the rainbow mirror ones, and the horse-lipped ones with spotted writing which we can't understand because the sea wrote it. And she walked down a long, white beach without looking back. And the sea was very gentle, and missed her like a sad dog with a smooth head.

Far away, where the blue changes to light, a centaur is crying as he paces towards her, his brown hands over his black eyes. His horse part is pure white and his tail's end is wet from the sea, which has stopped moving now and is listening to his hooves. Each of which are four golden centuries. He leaves a long stitch of time ticking behind him on the sands.

They get nearer and nearer and nearer, mother and the centaur, and when they meet he stops crying and he puts his brown arm around her white shoulder, and they look happy in a sad way, going up the beach together towards the land, and mother has her arm over his white horse's back. She is too light to have left any tracks, and the sea sighs and awakens like a cat. And licking forward, the sea gently wipes out the chiming hoof-prints left by the centaur.

And I was in my very beginning there, waiting to be born in the land they are walking to together, my mother and the wise centaur.

For nine years he had remained and nobody
knew him,
Carrying a shoe in his hand he went home
quietly, without ceremony.

We'll get up a party and all Go. That would *be*
fun.
Not Daddy
No, Daddy doesn't like the noise. His poor *head.*
Now, Deffy . . . Daddy's said no and he means it.
Now wait until you're a little *older, and you'll enjoy*
it so *much better   lots of little girls get all frighten-*
ed, you know ! By the clowns. And it's too far. And
in this heat too.

Oh dear —
          we've run out of bread
          that's funny — bread and circuses
               who said *that*

My days take me away like bread crusts lying
on the water, nibbled away by the swans on the
lake where Time's old man cuts the sedges under
a pink winter sky. He is brittle with frost, and dry
with the sawdust running out from his years, and
the swans are kings and queens waiting for him to
say the right word so that they can walk away from
their pile of white feathers, back to their snowy
kingdoms again. They lay their orange beaks on

his knee when he sits at the lake's edges, and one waits out on the water with one rowlock leg oared from its body, gloved in a black mackintosh skin. Their iron eyes demand with suspicions, but they pare away saying Frrip to each other, as they're forgotten all the words they used to rule with.

Now I have another birthday. I have seen it coming, pointing me out to my road, and with my other birthdays telegraphing me back and back over the heath, and swinging me down all the years. Until I come to my crossroads and a little stony track, where a man called Death looks out of a ruined cottage to see me coming.

When I roll with my eyes shut, the sun twists me around his little finger, over and over down the hill, with a flump at the bottom like jumping out of today into tomorrow. And to lie there is to hear him moving through the long grass like cows breathing summer up. And sometimes the warm morning will come and sit with you on the sun's doorstep, like an orange cat closed into himself by the sun's key.

A lorry climbs the hill and a lark removes it. A boy shouts in the valley and the brambles catch up his shout, and hang up a tattered song from the cowman, and a field has caught a dog and plays ball against his wall of barks. An aeroplane crawls over a cloud, like beetles on cow parsley, and another runs through the sky's white bushes like a bright silver fox, in and out with the sun's flashing teeth snapping a bite of light at its tail. Why do these things coming from so far put such a gold necklace of regret around your days, sad with all

126

mens' removed and forgotten wisdom, like smelling pinks by a brick path and one robin singing with rain a neighbour? Summer has a lifetime for daisies along the path, and winter blows its leaves against the white gate, and its rain makes baths for husband sparrows.

When these things happen, perhaps not only me lies in a buttercup cathedral while the day goes past me like a dog, riffling through the grass with long dusty ears closing his nose in. Perhaps someone who was me, dreaming me, said, down a long year. These things will happen and I will pass these on, dreaming a coming me. Saying Listen, O listen, new me. Or perhaps someone else has undone the golden necklace of regret, sighing as it falls into the buttercups and then saying Well, this won't do. All those animals walk away when they say this. And I must get on, picking up buckets or a cabbage or going into shops like ferrets, with cobweb eyes and breaking their celery's talk off, while the day goes on chewing everything up with its eyes closed in the sun. And nobody says Alas any more, like princesses.

O God, if you're there, why am I like a glass, brilliant with holding all the world, too easy to break with my heartache of so many stars? Because I'm truly praising with this, I say Dear God in crystal, holding the green earth in my clear glass, the water spiralling me into my crystal bubble, and the stars designing me with all their diamonds singing. I am cut out of their gonging night to circle my years like one minnow held up to the sun. Many birthdays are putting together my puzzle, and fitting

127

my rounded thoughts into place, and all my colours together. When I'm grown up I will be exactly fitted and smooth, and when I am old and gone over, I will be put into my coffin still held together with no breaks. Sums and worries are like bumps that won't drop into the holes, but a nice day fits its blue and green bits together like knowing its end.

> Go to sleep
> *I can hear you up there*
> Go to
> Sleep
> *No wonder you're always dreaming*
> *having nightmares*
> *what are you* doing
> *so pale in the morning*
> *Listen-to-each* WORD WORD
> *So pale in the Morning*
> *the Morning*
> *the Mourning*

Past my sleep there is an old man who shines like gold, and he waits for my coming in his cave. He watches the bright ferns outside, where the stream feels with a long white running hand over the rocks. He doesn't talk and I haven't one word of this world to say. He comforts with shining, and sits in the passed dusk behind the dust of all mens' minds swept off the summerhouse floor with one dry mouse and fingernail leaves by a twig broom. He doesn't get up, and he shows me by not being there.

Sometimes a tiger wets a paw in the stream, and sits down licking around his wrist on a wet rock, with his tail roped out of the water. He makes two leaps, and a fern spokes under his tread. He purrs and rubs his head on the rocks of the cave, and his tail goes swit, swit. He entices the darkness out into his eyes and pudds inside, sniffing at the old man's big toe, spidering his whiskers. Then he loosens his orange all over and flops down into a gathering of paws, rumbling like rolling fur barrels, and lowering his sleep like a chrysanthemum onto the old man's knee. Come, he says, and go.

I look in through an old iron gate in a stone wall, at many nuts trees growing behind a high century with sharksfin glass for stealers.

I think the nut trees would be in gold and silver like the King of Spain's umbrella, and the old man thinks me right as the nuts drop into the lemon grass. They do not need fairytales he says, as they are very old naturally, telling me to walk out through the other iron gate into a garden where there is a well bringing up no water for a ghost. The handle creaks with the sound, and the ghost knows there's only grass down the well, resting its powdered toadstool head on a hand of dried leaves.

Little hedges rule the pages of flowers from the choirs of cauliflowers, and the apple-trees bend with grey whispering to the old mulberry with its elbows in the grass, muttering of wizards. The garden tells me all the men have gone forever, and only the garden is left in the world. *Don't go*. Stay with us, for you are *the last one*. And if you go, then even the peacocks will fly over the walls, and the hunting sun will catch them to make a hat from their feathers. *Don't go*, for outside the world has gone away, and if you go too the old man in the cave won't think us any more, and we will tap ourselves into pieces like a dry coconut, and then even the ghost will fall out, leaving behind a smell of long evenings, and a warm dent in the squashed thyme.

But I'm already pulling the rusty bolt in the mouldy door of all the ages, by the paeonies and their bush of years where Time has dropped all its red petals. The last thing I shall see is the scythe propped by the wall where God has let all the apples rot, and remembering his brown, cracked and tiled hand that curled ratly around its handle, I shall rock open the palsied door of brick echoes and go out.

What do you say when I come to you with nothing?
Fling it down to the ground.
I said that I had nothing. What shall I let go?
If so, take it away.

Just look *at this report*
What does *she learn*

You'd think with the fees we're paying
        even though it is a Kindergarten I suppose
                really
No imagination Mrs. Leonard says
        just none   *arithmetic*
a complete block that other woman says   I don't
know it's all terribly *worrying*
        you don't suppose   no I don't   she's in any
        way

                        subnormal

In another sleep I have been a white tree, in a glass of brilliance, and I am a red leaf and a yellow leaf, and I am waiting for the wind to come. I am so *happy* I have gone into Light. The wind comes, O wind *come, come,* and I am going up where the blue has gone beyond white into a happiness of unending nothing. But I am also a green leaf, and must stay. Stay with the bright tree until death's wind comes again.

And I am eating my dinners and hanging up my clothes, and putting my mind into school tickets of yes and no and please and why Africa is hot, and poor old Neanderthal Man. And thank you, it's just what I want, and yes honestly, said straight like a striped tie.

And this other me, walking along looking at birch trees and beech trees and there's a sycamore, all pinging with knowledge and sticklebacks and chickweed. And how rubber comes on my boots and a plaster on my scratch. And smells of bacon and geraniums, and a corner of tom cat all hardening off into meaning no more Greece to the grownups. And the radio wearing a black and white coat of news to hang in my ears' cupboards, which I can listen to now without moths.

But how can I tell them about the black centaur, when I went up to see where the fire had been, dragoning into the night sky from the windows, and every bush a nest for phoenixes.

It is silent here, no birds singing and the wind has gone, leaving the sun picking about like a scorched vulture among the smoke forgetting. The ground is singed a rough furred black, like winter horses, and little grey lanes of smoke wave from the black antlers of the bitten trees. There is a blue roan smell and the sun looks up from the carcass like a quick antelope. Very old lions are somewhere near, sneezing and combing their noses with ash on their paws, their tails nerving the dust like someone brushing down stairs.

The black centaur trots out from the black trees with their half-burnt leaves held up like slices of dried oranges. He lifts his feet very high, puffing the hot ground with each dusty grey hoof. He stops when he sees me, his horse part very still. Then he stamps a hind leg, and flicks his black flank with his tail. His man part looks annoyed. Damn and damn. He didn't expect me. Then he walks towards me, stepping over the dead lion's ribs, and humming. He's going to say something in Greek, but then he looks thoughtful and picks his nose, wiping his finger on his glossy black rump. I want to ask him for a ride, but he has no mane to hold, only his muscled, brown back. And I know he only really wants a woman, even though he would never hurt me. He has trouble making his horse part work, and turns away so sharply that his legs step on themselves and he nearly trips, like a carthorse in a narrow lane.

Then he canters himself off with cheerful, tight farts from his happy black horse behind, flashing his tail and waving with one hand without looking back. It makes him laugh as he ducks under the trees into the wood. I can hear him galloping fast down one of the rides, splashing through the Naples-yellow bog, and kicking the ringing silence back like a dented clock. Then he must wait until a fire brings him out again, yawning into the sun's shaggy face, and stretching his brown arms while his horse bows down on all his four legs. He will scratch and rub his chest oh ah, and curl up one hind leg tightly at the end of all his stretch.

But who will see him then looking up like someone to come saying O *Look at the swallows*. You know someone will always say O Look at the swallows, or Look at the rooks, when the wind throws them up into the blue like gusts of charred paper from a bonfire. But who will stand there saying O look at the centaur, when he has brought himself back through a long dying think, not expecting the someone to see him back, their surprise balancing him into their eyes like two dangled cherries. Certain days, which have folded themselves down pig heavy with summer, will think a centaur back down an afternoon, resting his behind on an overgrown fence where once there was a field, and waving the flies off his doze with a picked foxglove. Just go by. *Just go by*, on quiet feet. He doesn't like his horse part to get a shy from suddenness. Which jerks his top into a hard awake. Never, never think him wicked, or all the men will wind up the black threads off the brambles to him, with murder running like a bleeding rabbit through the bushes, and they will kick summer away like a sack of ferrets, and whistle winter up like a white lurcher behind them. They will telegraph themselves across the wide fields knitted with snow, not looking at the hares splitting away like spilled beads. They will come to the black wood, with the red sun pushing through the twigs to watch too, before he must go, and they crack through it, hammering the trees like kettles.

And he will break, the black centaur, astonished at seeing winter outside, pricking his high legs through the snow, scratched by the thorns, and with a gorse bush caught up in his tail. He sprawls like a polar bear and rears up to the fence, plunging up and down to find a way out. They shout, and one greyhound has seen him, clutching the ground in gulping bounds, his spring tail winding him on. *That's him, that's him*, their shouts clap like pigeons in the white air, and they burst the centaur with their guns as he tries to jump. And they go away, over the snow in their boots, leaving him hanging on the brambles.

I know he has snowballs in his hoofs, and one leg is very slowly curling up. His tail shivers, and he looks at me. Don't look, *O don't look at me*, you're not really there, poor centaur.

But one of his hands is caught on the barbed wire, and the blood is drilling long red holes down into the snow.

And even if you don't think, centaurs take a long time dying out in us, dying back into their old summer, leaving our minds pressed into the snow like the Mah Jong footsteps of grey winter rabbits.

But in fallen leaves that have heaped the bare
      slopes,
How should I ever find his footsteps?

This fetish *for circuses*
It is *a fetish*
            its unnatural
last thing we wanted running into it like that round
      the bend
                  and there it was
You know she ran a temperature for two days
Two days which forgot the child
Forgot the child, suspended
in the hot hammock between the days and the
crawling dark salamander night.

And I missed one circus and another. Two.

They were coming up the hill from the holiday sea, and the engines won't stop even if dinosaurs come down from the rocks to stand all over the road in their knobs.

People walk beside the big lorries, and the engines with steam and bells and brass and whistling.

Slowly they bring their rolling Troy after them, full of lions again, and a whiptail of white mules with open mouths protesting into the hedges, and one Hosannah elephant hurrying to catch up, and two white horses with brown maps of Asia, and a twinkling of black Shetlands. O and look, there's not just one with spots, but *three;* one currant bun mother, one figgy father and a hundreds-and-thousands foal. They skitter by like shaken pepper, and that's all, except a ginger dog with guilty eyebrows from the village, eating what the elephant left for wheelbarrows.

They all go into a stony field and play for the sea below, where a fishing boat's sail is at ten to twelve, and the waves are making a long bed of sheets.

People grumble up the hills except the running children, and a monkey with an arched worry sits on a stone wall in a red jersey, shaking hands between his mind's hops.

He's caught a cricket, look, holding it up to bite like playing a small mouthorgan. We must. One day. . Not now, father gets a headache. . Wouldn't you like that peach flan. . Very soon dear. . But it's so *easy*, all you've got to do is *go*. O I've said, Please. Please. Please. Please. *Please*, like onward Christian Soldiers. No, dear wait for the big one at home.

I never get to the circus. One day you'll see, I'll ride a porridge-coloured horse with blue eyes past all your windows, with a red feather blowing, and diamonds on his bridle. And I won't look at you waving, riding over the green grass and telling him one two three, with his black legs like calendar girls in stockings in garages for red faced men.

I sit in the train. Father is asleep with an utterly fallen in through his letter-box, and Mother is looking at green coats in magazines, with people in pink baths.

Fields whistle up hedges and you jump them, mind the water, over the gate, through the ducks, round two black horses, over the quilted plough, hello red tractor, up with the sea gulls, but you can't stop, otherwise the train shoves Mother into them. Trees and farms and white sugar-lump houses, and one field has black and white cows and another has yellow cows, and they sit left where the train has toppled them all out of your flying time. The windows smell of egg and iron and the towns pass like opening books of chimneys, and a red bus falls away like losing a fish off the hook.

And the train stops by lavatory walls and by paintbox fruit shops, and irons past Cerberus and his red eyes in a tunnel.

Sometimes it stops at nowhere, like half-way through a stopped life, like half a dying. Sparrows dice and hop and spink, and thistles and long yellow grass are bending to hear a small wind, and a rosette of leaves has put up a green umbrella. People look out, yawning. Where are we, and reading. Everything is set out with God everywhere, and they *don't see*. One grass gentles another, flowers potter, stones lie between rabbits' ferns, here in white, and there in pink, and a black striped one near a primrose. You are in pink and white and in striped black too, with primroses and grass in your hands and feet, with sorrel and sparrow eyes, all in a Time which looks over the hedge like a cow at you, stopped chewing. Another Perfection, with God saying *There you are*, in spite of trains.

And people look down from bridges, with faces like white polyanthus, watching the big electric-eel train fizzing underneath them down its steel Nile, and a clattering backbone of trucks punching its fist all the way down to the guard in his jerked kennel.

A cup cannot float in the quantity of water
That will support a poppy-seed.

And then we're home, and everything stands back and has a look at us before it lets us in again, as though it dreamed when we went away and has to find its edges so that we can tuck them in again with our mind's blankets. When we wake up it's all back again, like two shillings down a china pig, clonk.

It's very strange before this happens, walking rather excuse me in the garden, and feeling round and sharp like a new penny in the retreated orchard like a heifer looking round, and all the trees holding away as though you're a coming beetle.

When you go to a new place, this happens at once, until it has had a sniff at you from behind like a strange black dog with uneasy yellow eyes, stiff with hard gathers. But when the place knows you and you know round the cats' eyelid corners, it settles back like a relaxed octopus and sighs itself out again with its eyes shut. And the birds let its dust fall again.

It's like a Pharaoh looking up out of a sleep, holding on to his snake hat with one hand, with a long black bull-terrier look. And turning over and going back to sleep again in a bed of gold dust.

And I missed the other circus, which was an old man and a cart and four black donkeys. He sang with his long white beard into the wind like Isaiah, and all his secret paper prophecies and potatoes were in sacks covered by a mackintosh. And he had some red cabbages, three fawn hens and a woolly little cockerel in a basket, a small dog like a squirrel with alas eyes, and a blotchy dog with blue eyes which sneaked at peoples' knees.

He also had a chocolate wife in the cart, with hair like mens' chests done up in a yellow duster, and they all puttered along the road trying to keep straight behind the donkeys. When they decided to stop, they all got out and the donkeys lay down and died and counted and whisked round in a small circle like angry spiders nipping time backwards round a hairy clock. And the dogs jumped and answered questions, and Isaiah sang about an Irish mother and made himself cry, and the hens just walked about, except for the little cockerel who couldn't get rid of a constipation, dipping and twitching his tail on feather-boa feet, and with a mauve effort on his face like a hard sum. They also had a piebald duck which rang a bell and was very rude *vrrrrt* in watery green on someone's sandals, and a bad-tempered monkey with tunnelling eyes and a Japanese rage very near. He has a chain, and paws like someone's black gloves shrunk with hands still inside, and he keeps his tail up like a masterful question. His lichen fur is powdered with green like old wooden gates, and he looks up and down in shutters.

The chocolate wife ends their circus, coming out from behind their cart and shaking out a sackfull of one big snake from among the potatoes, and look, she's taken off all her clothes. She heaves the spare bits of snake around her like a sailor looping up a boat on a quay.

She has two bits of unreal tiger over her chest and behind, which wobble under them like chocolate blancmanges, and her belly-button looks like a winkle sitting on a flat rock when she bends backwards. She rolls her eyes like Mr. Browning's bull, and shoos her mouth out like horses squeezing their last finish.

I heard Tom telling Cook about them, and Isaiah waved to me over the gate with a real prophet's Behold, and called me fair maiden like a daisychain, and shouted that beside him was the one and only Rose of Sharon, and his chocolate wife opened her teeth like a piano lid and held up an eclair thumb.

But I never got there, I just added up my hearing and made my own circus for my personal telling over. Mother said it's too small, dear. Wait for the big one. And Father said Mange is catching you'll bring something home disgusting exhibition see what all the fuss is about quite enough public spectacle think what the police are up to certainly not no daughter of mine Until my ears go into their caves.

Not a bad day then Liz
          eh
God perish these fucking asses   I swear I'll git
          back you
Hey Liz   *shut* up   *you fornicating bastard*
Know how to stop a donkey braying
          do you
                    eh
                              Liz
Liz?   Know how
Arabs do it   S'truth   an' the Eyetalians I'm tellin you   no str'uth   honest
Put a pata butter up their arse   donkey as to getta grip on is own arse-'ole like afore e can git the wind out t'other end   wonder if marge'd do

By the roadside, A Rose of Sharon;
The horse has eaten it.

And I waited, and I went to school and I *waited*. And I made six yellow cakes and a mistake for the birds, and I played with a young bloodhound sagged in a loose fur eiderdown, and with chamois leather ears and sentenced eyes, and she let out a harmonium when she saw a cow. And I *waited*. And I crayoned the Danube, and cut out the Grand Canyon, and I prayed every Prayers right and didn't let hymns go out like bees, but made a perfect sound-cabbage with every word and all my mouth. And I *waited*.

And I had Carol and Rosemary to tea and we played dog shows, and I won the Grand National on all fours. And I *waited*. And I went to Roderick's birthday party and we sawed on a chair leg instead of watching the conjurer. And I *waited*. And I fell down on the anthracite playground, and bled into the basin like waterpaint. And I *waited*. And Miss Gerald is growing a quiet yellow beard, and Doris had half a baby one afternoon in the middle of the onions, and dinner was late without gravy. And I *waited*. And all the gloxinias came out together in the greenhouse, like silent moose roaring Glory be to the Holy Ghost. And I *waited*.

And a great orange pig came into the garden and had eleven spotted piglets under the copper beech, white with black dots and dashes, and all exclaiming around their beached mother like hurried little typewritten sausages. *And I waited*.

And It's Coming !

But not to Mr. Browning's field, it's coming to the Common. It's so big it must go onto the Common, lifting itself like birthday cakes being brought in, cabled up to the sun for all its lights and humming with lions' hearts.

142

Everyone is waiting to go too, because there's
never been such a big one before.

There's rhinos and reindeer and hippos and horses
and gnus and giraffes and genets and caracals and
quaggas and oryxes and orang utans and onagers
and wild men and wolves and bontebeests and
buffaloes and Pallas' warthogs and wallabies and
brindled zebus and Ankole bulls and alligators and
Kodiak bears and kangaroos and kiangs and civets
and coypus and mandrills and musk oxen and
hartebeests and harp seals and phalangers and
pumas and lynxes and lorises and dik-diks and
dugongs and elands and elks and racoons and rattle-
snakes and tarsiers and turtles and skinks and sea-
lions and voles and vixens and unicorns and yaks
and perhaps a whale.

O, and the musical zebras Crying *Belshazzer and
Jezebel.*

It's really coming.
It's all really coming.
Thank you God. Really Amen this time to you.

Gee we'll have to go
    have to take her this time
What about the Pringles and the Downs' twins
    get them to come too
Well I'm not going alone
hate circuses
    can't get out of it this time
        ah all those smells

I feel so
faint   so
   so
useless
   no   flabby sort of
and embarrassed
      somehow
   I don't know   sort of feeble   and
            white
They're so different
            hard
never liked it as a child
                  even as a child
            oh that child

I went into the orchard to hold my whole circus think together in its beautiful cake, and I closed the white gate with its blink in the afternoon, and the sun was asleep on the lawn like a yellow retriever. The cows in the far field had hung up their patchwork under the trees, their shadows thrown over the hedges. Even the bees were struggling through the strings of heat curtaining their wings' way. One is fitted into a foxglove's doze, and another is snoring home to his hole giddy with the glare of buttercups.

Beneath the cherry blossoms
There are no
Strangers.

And under the apple tree I saw the Satyr watching me through the head of grass that he was holding against my shadow, watching me through the black keyhole of his stranger's eyes.

Come, come and sit down, said the Satyr. With me here. His teeth bit ladders up and down the grass stem, his side teeth pointed like a dog's. The grass left its seeds peppered on his beard. It started near his throat, in curling ones and twos like coming out of an old mattress, and joined hands all down his cheeks, and sealed down his upper lip like a funeral envelope.

You are a Satyr I said, looking at his squirrel ears, but I couldn't get into his eyes, they still had the key in, and I couldn't get my look past into his real room.

I am anything you like. Said the Satyr. If you say so. Yes, I am a Satyr. I have an apple for you. From behind his coat he brought out a red apple and held it out flat, like you do to horses. He had many tramways on his brown hand, and a gold snake ring with green eyes. But it's not time for our apples, there aren't any. Ah, said the Satyr. I asked the apple tree for you, before you came, knocking on her door and saying, Lady, Lady, make me an apple because I may need it one day when the sun is hot. And he laughed softly inside his jersey, like a horse seeing you out of his window. How did it grow? O said the Satyr. It grew *beautifully*. First she made a bunch of pink flowers, and she took one, and then she blew it up very slowly indeed, and she said, You can take the rest of the flowers home to your Mother. Go on, she said.

*Because I don't want anyone to know I've made
you one.* So I took the flowers. How? Did you go,
or did you send them to her? The Satyr scratched
a foxy armpit. I thought them into the cuckoo's
mate, and he dropped a green olive on her doorstep,
where she sits in her black shawl and her white
rubber shoes, with a cage of bright green birds on
the white wall, and a black goat is lying under a
cart full of lemons. O, I said. How did you become
a Satyr? Not rudely. Aren't you Pan? Great Pan,
Great Pan. Please, no, and *thank you*, said the Satyr,
digging in his ear and gently smelling his finger like
a dog over another dog's new. What do you do?
Now, I mean, out of Greece?

The Satyr rubbed his head on the trunk of the
apple tree, fixing his eyes with a drawing pin of
sky. It sounded like a billy goat's itch. I live in big
houses and I live in small houses and sometimes I
live in my cave. Do you eat and drink the same as
us? The Satyr snatched my apple back roughly and
bit it, using his corner teeth. You want to know,
you want to *know*, he said. Come here, then. Right
here, or I'll bite through the string and the sword
will fall.

O Love O Love, said the Satyr, taking off his coat
and making a pillow. His cigarettes fell out, and a
box of matches. Let's put the sun out he said, and
lit a match, holding it up to the sun who scorned
it into a little, black, kneeling man. The Satyr let
him twist his head over and die on his finger. *You*
did that, he said, *You* kiss it, you *hurt* me. He put
his finger with a black nail onto my mouth, and I
kissed it. He looked at it a long time like someone

146

feeling a bruise. If I could draw, I'd draw a mouth like yours. He pressed my teeth with his thumb. O bite me, he said, and a black leopard sat down near us. Bite me, and I'll show you how my black leopard kills the little fawn antelope. Look, you lead her on a red lead, and she has a little bell. And she cannot cry out with my claws in her throat. And we will drink her wine together, and I will make you a little dress from her soft skin. I promise. But I don't want to bite you, I said. No, that's quite right. *Quite true*, said the Satyr, pulling off a cobweb. We've got to be careful. *People are everywhere*. I thought of the centaur and I said, I hope you get back to Greece before they catch you. One day, one day, he said, but there's only one day when it happens. *It's only the one day*. You go down the narrow white street with its blue snake-skin shadows. Very white. *You know?* Yes, I said, I know. And all the way along there are red geraniums in boxes, and right at the top of all the steps there is a black bull with his wide horns chipping the houses. The sun is coming up the steps behind you, rolling up them like an orange octopus, feeling at the walls. What will you do? *O tell me what will you do*.

I'd go in through a door without ringing their brass bell, I said. *There aren't any doors*, said the Satyr, angrily. And all the windows have black shutters. The bull would fall down the steps and get up with his tail in the air, and he'd catch you on one horn and work at you like someone trying to pierce a bit of paper with a stick, and all the blood would hit the walls and run down the steps like red silk stockings.

147

No, I would be all geranium petals, I said. He wouldn't get me, I'd be all geranium petals, and the sun would be a cracked egg dropped from a basket.

People must never know, said the Satyr. O they won't, I said. They'll never know, because they don't even know about the angel. *Santa Maria!* said the Satyr, like a harp. What angel? O, he comes sometimes and reads his book here, and his sandals get quite wet after showers.

My mother, said the Satyr, *she* is an angel. She is with God all the time.

He squeezed me into his black jersey. *Blessed be the fruit of thy womb*, he said, stroking my hair and catching it on the gold snake. O, I said.

Don't move, *don't move*. He held me tightly, smelling of pumas. *Can you see them*, he said. It's all black, I said. Yes, all in black, walking with their shadows along the white wall, and for every woman there is a cypress on the roadside. Ten black women and ten black cypresses, and the white wall. They go one by one through the stone gateway under the broken lions, and far away in the glitter behind the groves the mind's dolphins are pulling the year away with them.

Perhaps they'll have a dolphin at the circus, I said, coming up from the Satyr's blanketing jersey. The Circus? Elephants don't ask questions, *elephants are friends of mine*, said the Satyr. I chain up their legs and scrub them, and they say Hello, Dionysio. But not *where's your papers*, and *your age*, and *your mad mother*, and girls to take down to my altar to show them my worries wrapped up in black paper, and a red velvet table with the golden chalice and its rubies all round it. That's for the first time, and the red velvet stops them screaming.

Do you look after an elephant? O do you? Then the Circus is really here. That's where you came from, as well as being a Satyr I mean. If you're a Satyr, how do you manage hiding your legs? I looked at his brown canvas shoes. They fit very well, does it feel queer having goat's hooves?

You talk, and *you talk*, said the Satyr. I give you an apple. Here. He sat up and took off his jersey, slowly, and he had a gold cross underneath. Now you, he said. No, I said. But I promised you a little dress of antelope, he said, and you ate all my apple. I will show you my hairy legs *all the way up and all the way down.*

I'm chained down by the terrible, licking sun. I'm unwinged like a grasshopper with snapped legs. *You mustn't tell.* You promised me a little antelope's skin. *Look. Here. And look.*

Slowly he kneels up and undoes his belt with eagles' wings on it. He has run all the way from Greece.

You are like a nest of little white rabbits, said the Satyr, unlocking his eyes with a twisted black church key.

The sun scorches my legs pegged out of his shadow. Please. *Please*, he said. *Love me.*

Mother and father have run away, and the grassy viper stings. An ant runs over my thigh. There are stones under my neck. O, apple tree. *Apple tree.*

His tongue is like a starfish, and his hair is over my chest smelling of oiled sheep. He bites through

149

the string, and the sword falls, as he said. O apple tree. *Never dream me again. Never again. Never.*

He wipes me with his handkerchief.

What do you want, says the Satyr, with his voice full of empty sacks. Come. Tell me. My little bird. No crying now, what would you like. *O holy angels.* I always say O holy angels when I scrub my elephants' sins with green soap, until their ears are spotted and pink like orchids.

He fastens my dress wrong, and I get my socks on, and my elastic is broken so I can't wear them. I hide them in some nettles.

We must go back now. Or they'll wonder. To the Circus? Yes, Dionysio has come back, they will say. Will you please take me to the Circus? *Will you?* You promised me my skin, but I'd rather have one last circus.

The Satyr undoes a mauve sweet, and holds it up to the sun, then gives it to me and gives himself a cigarette. We go out of the orchard, and the apple tree puts back the afternoon like someone putting down a toad. Over the fields and out to the Common, the Satyr holding my hand. You're not really a Satyr, I say. I wish you hadn't, and you hadn't *said.*

Men and Satyrs, all different, all the same. Twinkle, little star, how I *wonder* what you are, said the elephants' son.

Lucy, Siam, Queeny, here's your Dionysio back. They sway and clank, and throw straw at me, and are jealous. I'm afraid of them reaching with their hoovers.

Somewhere a lion is coughing like someone pumping blood into a sealed room, until it trickles out through the keyhole, and then with a thick splash forces out the key. It has dropped into the blood and I cannot pick it up. I cannot. *I cannot.*

Yes, yes ! I answered,
But someone still knocked
At the snow-mantled gate.

Men come and take me to see the horses being harnessed, and call me Dino's friend. *No one asks.* I watch the people come in. I watch the circus. The seat is right on the edge of their world, and camels and horses shake froth onto me.

I mustn't ever tell, even though all the centaurs and all the Satyrs are bone dead. And the angel will never come back, and the walnut tree will go on without me.

The awful thing was I never gave him my diamond. *I didn't know how.*

People bounce under lights off see-saws, and ride bicycles, and bears ride bicycles, and a clown touches me like a dead man.

I don't want any more touching, I will dry myself and dress myself, and do up my shoes, and keep my crystal back without cracks.

There are sand coloured horses looking angry, and flicking whips, and a llama jumping over hoops. There is Pontius Pilate standing on three white horses, and I *still love horses*. There are four blacks and four marmalades, and four memorial greys, and four Persian bays with princely legs, and four snaking, spotted horses, the best of them all.

There are two giraffes surprised at a high wisdom, and people swinging high up, and I've got a sore throat, looking.

There's a car banging and hosing people, and men catching women on chairs with a clup, and two men walking on washing lines. And Chinese with plates and bends, and Judgement Day hanging over the elephants. And lions and tigers wrinkling, and polar bears slipping their fur about as they turn. And sea-lions, and then I leaned into a hard, fenced sleep.

They woke me up. *Come on, ducks. It's over.* It's all over, and I am hurting with an old heart.

It was only people showing through like a spoilt cathedral.

I went back over the fields, and the cows had come out to graze in the middle, and the swallows were drinking in the pink pond under the pink sky. Two bats were leathering at the edge of the wood, *fitter fitter spik.*

Wherever have you been. We've been out of our minds with worry. You're never to do this again Ever again   What happened   *Whatever happened*

I think she enjoyed it
   don't you   oh   yes
but after all that fuss *she   I don't know*

hardly a word   well she felt sick in the morning
of course
         yes
      She's very quiet
       today
       m'mm
     Did she
   I mean   I wonder
     did she say
     anything
       no
         stared and stared at the elephants side
everywhere   horribly embarrassing
   NO
     she didnt say anything
     Why?   Why?
 oh   *nothing*

I went to the circus. I went to the circus. It was very nice. It was a circus. It was full of just circus, and God held back the curtains for the elephants.

And God never saw my sparrow.

And now I can see winter and summer meeting like two old countrymen down a long blue road under copper beeches. One walks away, and the other turns off down a lane and up a hill, and then there's only the road.

A dog jumps onto the road and runs after one of them and the blue road waits unmoved, like wildebeest watching.

A shower from a mauve cloud in a turquoise sky.

A pheasant winds up. Summer has lit a lamp high up on the downs in his cottage. It is dusk. But winter is still on the road, with a sack over his shoulders and the dark at his heels like a collie.

The sky is clear now through the trees, and they drip quietly onto the white road. It's cold, and a thin moon is hooked on the edge of the black wood above summer's topaz window. Her reflection curls in the puddle, like an Ayreshire's dropped horn.

The road waits for me. With a twittering of shrews under the saxifrage leaves, the road waits.

For me. Now. And with all God's puzzle joined and knowing into forever and ever, Amen.

The road and me knowing forever backwards and forwards and in one drop of rain.

Now. Me. In one drop of the rain.

The wind gives me
Enough fallen leaves
To make a fire.

END